PLANT
PATHOGENS

THE SOCIETY FOR APPLIED BACTERIOLOGY
TECHNICAL SERIES NO. 12

PLANT PATHOGENS

Edited by

D. W. LOVELOCK

*H. J. Heinz Co. Ltd, Hayes Park, Hayes,
Middlesex, England*

1979

ACADEMIC PRESS
LONDON · NEW YORK · SAN FRANCISCO
A Subsidiary of Harcourt Brace Jovanovich, Publishers

ACADEMIC PRESS INC. (LONDON) LTD.
24/28 OVAL ROAD
LONDON NW1

U.S. Edition Published by
ACADEMIC PRESS INC.
111 FIFTH AVENUE
NEW YORK, NEW YORK 10003

British Library Cataloguing in Publication Data

Society for Applied Bacteriology.
  Autumn Demonstration Meeting,
  National College of Food Technology,
  1976
  Plant pathogens. – (Society for Applied
  Bacteriology. Technical series; no. 12).
  1. Micro-organisms, Phytopathogenic
  I. Title II. Lovelock, Dennis William III. Series
  581.2′3   SB734   78–73887

  ISBN 0–12–457050–X

Printed in Great Britain by
Latimer Trend & Company Ltd, Plymouth

Contributors

R. P. ADAMS, *Agricultural Development and Advisory Service, Woodthorne, Wolverhampton*

ADEBOLA O. ADEGEYE, *Agriculture Building, The University of Leeds, Leeds, Yorkshire LS2 9JT, England*

EVE BILLING, *East Malling Research Station, East Malling, Maidstone, Kent, England*

E. S. P. BROMFIELD, *Department of Agricultural Botany, University College of Wales, Aberystwyth, Wales*

M. J. DANIELS, *John Innes Institute, Colney Lane, Norwich, Norfolk NOR 7OF, England*

LYNDA M. FLETCHER, *Biology Department, King Alfred's College, Winchester, Hampshire, England*

D. GARETH JONES, *Department of Agricultural Botany, University College of Wales, Aberystwyth, Wales*

D. C. HARRIS, *East Malling Research Station, East Malling, Maidstone, Kent, England*

BARBARA M. LUND, *ARC Food Research Institute, Colney Lane, Norwich, Norfolk NOR 7OF, England*

P. G. MARKHAM, *John Innes Institute, Colney Lane, Norwich, Norfolk NOR 7OF, England*

R. W. POLLEY, *MAFF Plant Pathology Laboratory, Hatching Green, Harpenden, Hertfordshire, England*

T. F. PREECE, *Agriculture Building, The University of Leeds, Leeds Yorkshire LS2 9JT, England*

MURIEL E. RHODES-ROBERTS, *Department of Botany, University College of Wales, Aberystwyth, Wales*

I. ROBINSON, *Agricultural Development and Advisory Service, Woodthorne, Wolverhampton*

R. TOWNSEND, *John Innes Institute, Colney Lane, Norwich, Norfolk NOR 7OF, England*

W. C. WONG, *Agriculture Building, The University of Leeds, Leeds, Yorkshire LS2 9JT, England*

Preface

This volume includes contributions to the Autumn Demonstration Meeting of the Society for Applied Bacteriology held in October 1976 at the National College of Food Technology, Weybridge, Surrey. It is Number 12 in the Technical Series and continues the Society's policy of encouraging members and guests to exhibit methods that are of value in the day-to-day work of the laboratory. The demonstrators have described their methods in this book which is intended to be a reference book on the laboratory bench rather than on the library shelves. We wish to thank them all for the great efforts which they took in the preparation of these demonstrations and for their contributions in this book.

Several factors prolonged the gestation period of this member of the Technical Series but it is hoped that the impact of the authors' contributions have not been muted in consequence. The Society is greatly indebted to Dr. T. F. Preece and Mr. C. H. Collins, M.B.E. for their prodigious efforts to expedite publication.

Our thanks go also to Professor E. Rolfe, Principal of the National College of Food Technology, and those members of his staff who contributed so much to the success of the Demonstration Meeting.

January 1979

D. W. Lovelock
R. Davies

Contents

Diagnosis of Watermark in Willows and Some Characteristics of *Erwinia salicis* (Day) Chester

T. F. PREECE, W. C. WONG AND ADEBOLA O. ADEGEYE

Agriculture Building, The University of Leeds, Leeds, Yorkshire, England

An illustrated account is available of the symptoms of watermark disease of cricket bat willows (Preece, 1977). These are: wilting of the foliage, reddening and browning of the leaves, die-back of the branches of varying severity, excessive proliferation of very leafy shoots below the die-back and occasional production of bacterial ooze where small branches join larger ones. The disease is progressive, but trees are rarely killed completely. In addition to external symptoms, red-brown, becoming black, internal staining (together with marked weakening of the wood in these areas) gives the disease its name, and is the symptom on which presumptive diagnosis in the field is based under the eradication legislation now in existence in England.

The cricket bat willow tree is normally sterile. Thus, it can only be propagated by taking cuttings from existing trees. Vegetative propagation of any crop means that all the plants are genetically homogeneous and uniformly susceptible to disease. The single willow cultivar in use, *Salix alba* var. *caerulea*, is the only commercially acceptable material for making cricket bats available at the present time.

The area where cricket bat willows grow well in the UK is almost entirely restricted to East Anglia, and there trees are most frequently planted in succession on the same sites near waterways in a kind of continuous "mono-culture". The disease is found on some wild willows and also on trees planted for their amenity value (*Salix alba, S. alba* var. *tristis, S. caprea, S. cinerea, S. purpurea, S. vitellina* and a hybrid, × *S. vividis*). The disease is, however, most severe and widespread on the cricket bat willow (*S. alba* var. *caerulea*), and field survey evidence seems to indicate that the source of the troublesome disease in general in the UK is in the cricket bat willows themselves, not in wild or amenity willows.

Since, as will be discussed later, considerable variation in *Erwinia salicis* is easily detectable, all the information briefly noted above adds up to the cricket bat willow—*E. salicis*—environment interaction being one of very high disease risk in which severe losses will occur if a more pathogenic variant of *E. salicis* should become prevalent. In addition to the obvious need to know and understand watermark disease, the development of control procedures other than eradication including the consideration of other genotypes of *Salix* for commercial exploration in cricket bat making (or even other types of wood altogether) would be wise, in the light of experience in other crop disease situations where the "genetic base" of the desired plant is very narrow as it is in this case.

Legislation is, however, likely to remain the principal means of containing the disease in the UK, the destruction of watermarked trees being enforced under a statutory instrument covering eastern England— The Watermark Disease (Local Authorities) Order, 1974. This order is at present undoubtedly most valuable in keeping down the number of trees developing symptoms in the field each year (for example in Essex to 200–300) and the detection of diseased mother trees in that county (used as sources of propagating material) to 5–10 a year. The situation is not as easy to control by eradication (of diseased trees) as is the case in other crops, because of the long period (commonly 5–7 years) between infection and the development of detectable symptoms. Thus at any time a considerable number of apparently healthy infected trees exist, which do not show symptoms until several years later. Symptomless, but infected, wood contains massive numbers of the cells of the pathogen. The use of bacteriological procedures is the only way of detecting the "symptomless carrier" situation in this disease.

Since 1970, several aspects of watermark disease have been under active investigation at Leeds and in Essex. These include epidemiology and related topics; histochemistry together with changes in certain enzymes and phenols; field surveys and susceptibility testing together with studies of new control measures. Much of this material is in process of publication elsewhere, or is part of unpublished research theses. The objects of this paper are to present techniques which have been found to be useful in diagnosis which may be useful to others and also to review the information available to date on the observed characteristics of the bacterium which causes the disease in willows.

Isolation of *Erwinia salicis* from Suspect Material

Old die-back lesions on definitely watermarked trees contain a great variety of bacteria. This was confusing to the early workers on the disease. Metcalfe (1940), for example, gave details of four different bacteria which he isolated from diseased willows, only one of which could be shown to be pathogenic, and was *E. salicis*. As has been experienced in recent years in the Netherlands the difficulties of isolating *E. salicis* from long-standing, advanced infections in, for example, a town street, are considerable because of this plethora of micro-organisms. The ease with which we have been able to isolate *E. salicis* in pure culture from cricket bat willows at Leeds in recent years is because of the efficiency of the willow inspectors working under the Statutory Order in their finding the first visible external, red-leaf symptoms in the field. Because of frequent inspections under the Statutory Order, the finding of an old decayed watermark diseased tree in the UK is becoming increasingly rare.

Young branches and shoots (preferably still with green bark) from affected parts of the tree are the best material from which to attempt isolation of *E. salicis*. Specimens can be stored at 4° for considerable lengths of time before isolation is attempted.

Partial sterilization of the outer surface of a piece of shoot (about 2 cm in diameter by 10 cm long) by dipping in 95% alcohol and then quickly flaming reduces contamination significantly. Using aseptic precautions the bark is quickly peeled off, the piece of wood cut in two and sap squeezed from the freshly cut surface using sterilized pliers. The sap is then plated out directly onto glycerol nutrient agar, (1% glycerol incorporated into Oxoid nutrient agar is suitable). Direct microscopical examination of squeezed-out sap, best done in distilled water and using phase contrast, will show numerous, usually visibly motile bacteria. In almost all cases a slide agglutination test (see p. 5) can be performed, and often a direct Gram stain shows that the organism is present in pure culture, as a Gram-negative short rod. Some of the colonies of *E. salicis* may not appear on the glycerol nutrient agar (GNA) until five days have elapsed at 26°. Most commonly, colonies of *E. salicis* are discrete, 1–2 mm in diameter, smooth, transparent and golden yellow honey coloured. The yellow pigment is best produced on subcultures onto potato plugs or 0·5% starch potato agar at a pH of 6·5, but, not only do some pathogenic isolates of *E. salicis* not produce pigment, but also the majority of the isolates lose the ability to produce it on continuous subculture on glycerol nutrient agar. Subcultures of individual colonies are then examined further by biochemical, phage and serological tests. The metabolism of *E. salicis* is respiratory and fermentative; other reactions are considered in detail later.

Detached Shoot Test for the Confirmatory Diagnosis of Watermark Disease in the Laboratory

Confirmatory diagnosis of bacterial plant diseases must involve a host pathogenicity test. This is difficult in the case of watermark disease.

Day (1924), Dowson (1937) and Metcalfe (1940) reported that it took several months to a year for the disease to show symptoms in artificially infected trees. The shortest time in which Wong (1974) reported any symptoms was 14 weeks after the inoculation of two-year-old cuttings. Much more detailed work by Adegeye (1975) has shown extreme variability in the production of symptoms in artificially inoculated, rooted $1\frac{1}{2}$-, $2\frac{1}{2}$- and $4\frac{1}{2}$-year-old cuttings. In six months, only 7% of artificially inoculated willows produced the typical intense internal staining of the wood as seen in field infections, 45% developed very slight internal staining and 48% did not show any staining at all. Similarly only 11% of inoculated cuttings eventually produced the red-leaf symptom.

Wong (1974) placed unrooted healthy willow shoots in test tubes containing suspensions of *E. salicis*. This was found to consistently result in brown discoloration of the cut ends of the shoots in 12 days, which was considerable advance on the erratic results with rooted host tests reported above (taking, at the earliest, 14 weeks).

Performance of detached shoot test

Care in setting up the test is essential. The outer surfaces of cricket bat willow shoots of not more than 2 cm in diameter and about 20 cm long are wiped over with cotton wool soaked in 95% alcohol. Using flamed secateurs cut off a shoot placed beneath the surface of sterile distilled water in a deep dish. The cut end, still beneath the water is covered with a small plastic test tube, itself filled with water. Each shoot, standing in water in the small plastic tube during handling, is placed in a large boiling tube containing 25 ml of a 48-hour-old suspension of the organism being tested (10^9 cells ml^{-1}) in nutrient broth. The small plastic test tube is removed from the end of the detached shoot with sterile forceps under the surface of the bacterial suspension. The mouth of the boiling tube is sealed with transparent plastic film and wrapped in black light-proof plastic film. Our tests have been conducted in duplicate, with controls, in a Prestcold controlled environment cabinet at 75% RH, $22°$ and a 16-hour day period of 34 000 lux, with the boiling tubes containing the cuttings supported in wooden racks. Small quantities of sterile nutrient broth are added aseptically from time to time to prevent drying out. Wood discoloration with suspensions of *E. salicis* is apparent by day 10 and is usually intense by 14 days. The test cuttings are best cut cleanly a short distance from the base for examination, and left exposed to the air for 5 to 10 hours. All pathogenic isolates of *E. salicis* have given discoloration which is quite undistinguishable from that seen in natural infections. In 205 tests, for example, in conjunction with agglutination tests and attempted isolations on GNA, the shoot test was positive in 203 out of 205 tests when agglutination and isolation tests were positive. No false positive tests have been seen. Further use of this detached shoot test is desirable. It is almost certain that the controlled environment used is not necessary, and it may be possible to store the shoots ready for use as Billing *et al.* (1960) did with the green pear fruits they used for testing *E. amylovora* isolates.

Field Slide Agglutination Tests

Although useful for certain virus diseases, the use of bacterial antisera in sap agglutination tests in the field has not been developed, though Graham (1963), for example, has shown it to be useful in the diagnosis of potato blackleg. We have used this method extensively in the field for the detection of *E. salicis* infections (Wong and Preece, 1973) in standing trees, leafy shoots arising from the stumps of felled trees and in the decaying wood of stumps. Field Slide Agglutination Tests (F.S.A.T.) should always be used in conjunction with simultaneous attempts to isolate the pathogen in GNA. It is of course the speed with which the test can be done which makes it valuable and by means of its use it is possible to detect infection in the field when the "classical" symptoms are absent (such as wood staining).

Production of antiserum and use in the field

The antisera used were prepared in rabbits without adjuvant by intravenous injection using a suspension of formalin and (1×10^{10} cells ml^{-1}) *E. salicis*. Titres were usually $\pm 1/640$. No preservative was added to the separated serum and it was stored in 1 ml quantities in small vials at $-20°$. It was taken to the field in a frozen solid form in a Dewar flask. Drops of sap were squeezed onto glass slides from the cut ends of shoots, using pliers. One drop of sap and one drop of antiserum showed good positive agglutination, visible instantaneously. Control slide tests were performed on each batch of antiserum. All slow or difficult to interpret reactions were considered as negative.

Table 1, taken from Wong and Preece (1973) shows the type of result obtained using this procedure in the field and the results of 112 detached shoot tests and of attempts at isolation of the pathogen on GNA. Six trees gave a positive F.S.A.T. but *E. salicis* was not isolated on GNA, one gave a negative F.S.A.T., but was positive on GNA (it was a decayed stump). In 82 cases presented here the F.S.A.T. and GNA results were both positive, and in 23 cases the F.S.A.T. and GNA results were both negative.

TABLE 1. The results of slide agglutination tests performed in the field using *Erwinia salicis* antiserum and the sap from trees of cricket bat willow and other *Salix* spp. compared with the symptom picture, the results of culturing sap on glycerol nutrient agar (GNA) and detached shoot tests

Species of *Salix*	Tree symptoms	No. tested	Field sap agglutination test		Isolation on GNA		Detached shoot test on isolates	
			+ve	−ve	+ve	−ve	+ve	−ve
Salix alba var. *caerulea*	None	17	10	7	10	7	10	7
	Red leaf only	5	2	3n.t.	5	0	5	0
	Wood stain only	16	16	0	15	1	15	1
	Red leaf and wood stain	41	41	0	38	3	38	3
	Tree dying, looks like *Armillaria* attack	9	2	7n.t.	6	3	6	3
	Leafy old stumps, with no symptoms on leaves	4	4	0	4	0	4	0
	Decayed stumps	7	4	3	2	5	2	5
S. fragilis	None	13	10n.t.	3	0	13	0	0
S. caprea	None	18	11n.t.	7	0	18	0	0
S. caprea	Red leaf and wood stain	9	9	0	9	0	9	0
S. vitellina	Red leaf and wood stain	6	6	0	6	0	6	0
Salix spp. (not identified)	None	11	7n.t.	4	0	11	0	0
Salix spp. (not identified)	Severe die-back and wood stain	1	1	0	1	0	1	0

n.t., not tested.

The Indirect Fluorescent Antibody Test for *Erwinia salicis*

The principles (Preece, 1971a, 1971b) and procedures for plant pathogenic fungi (Preece and Cooper, 1969) have been reviewed elsewhere.
The indirect or "sandwich" procedure is more sensitive than the direct
procedure in which the labelled antibody is applied directly to slides
(bearing smears or sections) carrying the antigen. The indirect procedure
is as follows. Reaction of unlabelled antibody with the antigen is allowed
to occur and fluoroscein-isothiocyanate labelled anti-rabbit globulin
from a commercial source applied. As usual, the slide is viewed using
u.v. light and a dark-ground condenser.

Best results with cricket bat willow wood were obtained using sections
of frozen wood cut in a cryostat (Adegeye, 1975) and on smears heat-fixed
in the usual way on specially cleaned slides (Georgala and Boothroyd,
1968).

Preparation of willow wood sections

Freshly cut 1cm³ blocks of infected wood were placed in 5% aqueous
polyvinyl alcohol (BDH Ltd) to facilitate sectioning and reduce freezing
damage. A metal blockholder was pre-cooled to —25° in a cryostat
cabinet (Bright Instruments Ltd). A few drops of embedding medium
for frozen tissue specimens (Ames O.C.T. Compound, R. A. Lamb Ltd),
was used to hold the block on the holder, and a fast CO_2 freezing unit
(Slee Medical Equipment Ltd) used to cool the block to —60°. More
embedding medium was added so as to cover the entire block. Transferred to the cryostat, the mounted block was sectioned (18 μm) at
—25°. The sections were mounted on slides smeared with Haupt's
adhesive (Purvis *et al.*, 1966), air-dried and kept in a closed plastic box
until stained. Wood more than two years old was softened, and sectioning much improved by using the procedure described by Sharon (1973),
i.e. fixing the wood in formal-acetic-alcohol for 2 hours, rinsing in tap
water for 4 hours, and storing in glycerol and 50% ethyl alcohol (1:1, v/v)
for at least 2 days before sectioning.

Using a suitable dilution of the test reagents

The high cost of the fluorescein labelled anti-rabbit immunoglobulin is
such that the use of optimal dilutions is necessary for economy if a
number of samples are to be tested. The optimal dilution is that which
gives intense specific staining and negligible background fluorescence.

The range of dilutions over which the reagent is effective is stated by the manufacturer (e.g. Wellcome Research Laboratories; Lot K9358, 1:4 to 1:16). Usually the antiserum was most satisfactory undiluted and the labelled globulin at 1:9 (i.e. 10^{-1}).

Preparation of phosphate buffered saline

Following Walker *et al.* (1971) solutions of Na_2HPO_4, 1·4 g in 100 ml distilled water and of $NaH_2PO_4.H_2O$ of the same strength, are made up. 84·1 ml of the first solution is mixed with 15·9 ml of the second solution, 8·4 g of NaCl added and the volume made up to 1 litre.

Staining procedure

Marking the location of material on slides by the use of a diamond saved much time when the preparations were examined under u.v. light using a dark-ground condenser. Slides with sections or smears for staining were stored on a metal rack in a plastic box containing a mat of wet absorbent tissue paper. After adding one drop of the anti-*E. salicis* antiserum, the slides remained in a plastic box in an incubator at 37° for 30 min. Excess antiserum was washed off by rinsing in phosphate buffered saline, and by gentle agitation for 20 min in Coplin jars containing this buffer solution (2 changes of buffer, 10 min each). Slide preparations were dried by gently blotting with filter paper, which was discarded after each preparation. One drop of the diluted F.I.T.C.-labelled anti-rabbit globulin was placed on the dried smear or section. After blotting they were mounted in buffered glycerol (9 parts glycerol:1 part buffered saline) and examined or photographed immediately. Many different controls (e.g. healthy wood, other bacteria in the wood and non-immune serum) have been used from time to time. Some of these should be tested with each batch of antiserum and test reagent used.

All preparations were examined at— $\times$ 500 or $\times$ 1000 magnification using dark-ground fluorescence in a Patholux Fluorescence Microscope (Vickers Ltd). A blue light passing primary filter (1 mm thick, B.G.12) with an upper barrier filter (1·5 mm, O.G.4) and a lower barrier filter (1·5 mm, G.G.9, $+1·5$ mm clear glass) gave beautifully clear results with very little autofluorescence. Using a 35 mm camera unit and Agfacolour 50L Professional film, the best exposure time for contrast was $1–2\frac{1}{2}$ minutes.

Specific, very bright, yellowish-green fluorescence was observed only in sections from infected wood, mainly inside the vessels which were located in or near the dark brown stained areas. Some vessels are filled

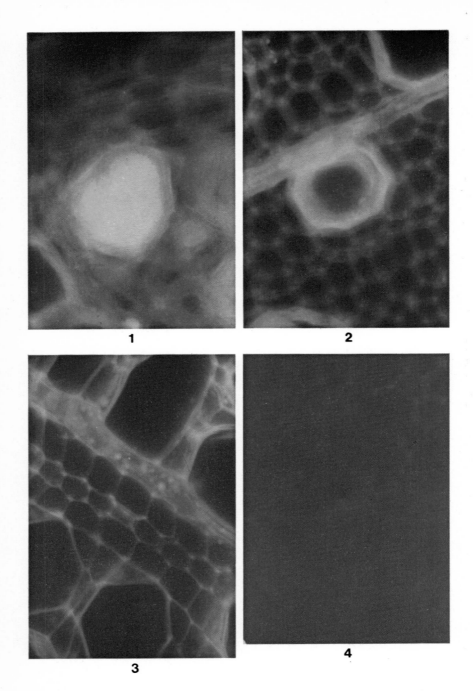

1

2

3

4

with specifically staining bacteria (Plate 1), others are lined with thicker or thinner layers of bacteria (Plate 2). Some cells in the diseased area show an unusual reddish-brown fluorescence (Plate 1). Specific staining was also found inside other tissues in the wood, such as rays (Plate 3), fibres, and parenchyma cells. Leaf trace bundles were also seen to contain specifically stained bacteria. In stained control sections using the filters described above, autofluorescence of the wood was negligible (Plate 4).

The Toluidine Blue Staining Method Applied to *Erwinia salicis* Infections of Willow Wood

None of the methods devised so far for staining bacteria in infected plant tissue (such as that of Stoughton, 1930) are particularly reliable or rapid to use. The use of toluidine blue by Wong (1974) to stain *E. salicis* in willow wood seems to have been an important practical development in the study of bacterial plant diseases. Toluidine blue, synonymous with toluidine blue O and methylene blue T50 or T extra (Conn and Lillie, 1969) is a basic dye of the thiazine series prepared from *o*-toluidine, sodium thiosulphate and dimethyl-*p*-phenylene diamine. It is a water-soluble green powder, molecular weight 305·85, called "tolonium chloride" by Stecher *et al.* (1968).

Shoemaker and Riddell (1954) first used toluidine blue in plant pathology—to stain *Streptomyces scabies* in potato scab. Apart from this, and being used to stain bacteria in milk (Moats, 1961) it does not seem to have been used for staining bacteria in plant tissues or elsewhere. It stains preparations made from pure cultures of fungi well, especially their chromosomes and nucleic acids, being used by Townsend, (1957) for yeasts and by Marks, (1965) for *Phytophthora infestans*. It was first used to stain plant tissues invaded by fungi in studies at Leeds of maize tissues infected by *Ustilago maydis* (Callow and Ling, 1973) and since then by Ghemawat (1977) for *Erysiphe graminis* infections of wheat leaves. It seems that certain virus infections of plants can be detected by toluidine blue staining (Meenakshi *et al.*, 1972) and it is a reliable stain for woody

PLATES 1–3. Portions of transverse sections of infected cricket bat willow wood collected from the field and stained using the indirect fluorescent antibody technique as described in the text (× 250).
PLATE 1. Shows specific bright yellowish green fluorescence filling a vessel. Reddish-brown, non-specific fluorescence is seen in cells at the bottom of the plate. In Plate 2, specific staining is seen as a thick band lining a vessel. Some ray cells are infected. Fig. 2 shows specific staining in ray cells and parenchyma cells at a distance from the vessels.
PLATE 4. Pale light green autofluorescence of control, uninfected wood.

and non-woody plant materials fixed and embedded in a variety of ways (Sidman *et al.*, 1961; O'Brien *et al.*, 1964; Feder and O'Brien, 1968; Hoefert, 1968; Marks 1973; Sakai, 1973). It is a good rapid temporary stain for diseased material generally, and as a permanent stain, the ease with which sections (still in wax) can be beautifully stained by the inexperienced, is most useful. The dye solution may be made up as 0·05% toluidine blue (British Drug Houses Ltd) in 0·1 M phosphate buffer at pH 6·8. Hand or cryostat sections are stained for 1 min, rinsed in distilled water and mounted in water. "Ringing" the coverglass with nail-varnish prevents the preparations drying up. Such preparations can be made permanent (Wong, 1974) by carefully rinsing, rapidly, in 40% w/v formaldehyde solution for 30 seconds after staining, dehydrating through a graded series of alcohols, (50, 75, 90, 95, 100% ethyl alcohol) allowing 1 or 2 min in each, cleaning in xylene and mounting in canada balsam. Paraffin wax sections, mounted on slides using Haupt's adhesive are best stained in the wax on the slides (Adegeye, 1975) for 10 min, washed in water for 1 min, air dried and the wax removed in 4 changes of xylene, allowing 30 min in each change of xylene, and finally mounting (directly from xylene) into neutral mounting medium (G. T. Gurr Ltd).

Erwinia salicis stains dark blue to royal blue. Much of the woody tissue stains greenish blue. Bacteria are found in a characteristic pattern in watermarked willow wood. They are contained in relatively few heavily stained scattered vessels, easily picked out with the dark blue masses of bacteria within them (Fig. 1). Few vessels are filled with bacteria; more usually they form a layer round part or whole of the inner surface of vessels (Fig. 1). Usually only one of the 2–6 cells of a pore-multiple in the wood contains *E. salicis*. More rarely the bacteria are seen in parenchyma cells associated with vessels, a few fibres, medullary ray cells and vessels of leaf trace bundles. Tyloses are not common in *E. salicis*-infected wood. The pattern, caused by the curious irregular scattering of infected vessels in transverse sections (Fig. 1) is useful in diagnosis. The use of mere sophisticated fixation, resin embedding and toluidine blue staining procedures for both light and transmission electron microscopy is described fully by Callow and Ling (1973).

FIG. 1. Natural *Erwinia salicis* infections of cricket bat willow wood rapidly stained in material collected from the field. These are cryostat sections 20 μm thick, permanently mounted in canada balsam (Wong, 1974). (a) × 150, shows the typical pattern of scattered vessels packed with *E. salicis*. (b) × 1250, shows masses of bacteria coating the vessel walls and in ray cells. These preparations still showed dark blue to royal blue staining of the bacterium and pale greenish blue staining of the wood after 5 years storage.

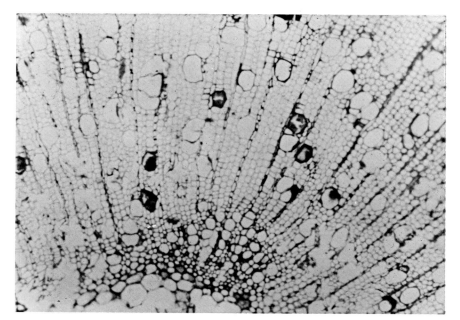

FIG. 1 (a)

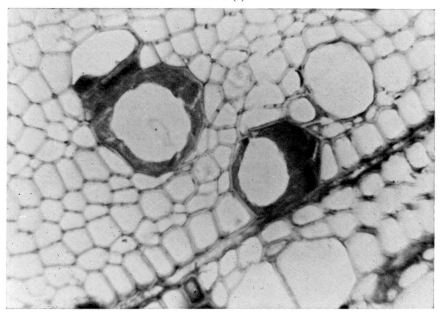

FIG. 1 (b)

Some Characteristics of Isolates of *Erwinia salicis*

Erwinia salicis was first isolated during the early 1920s in Essex (Day, 1924). It is not certain how long the disease had been present there. Dowson (1937) extended the work, and confirmed the causative organism as *E. salicis*. Metcalfe (1940) worked on the disease in East Anglia and had difficulty in distinguishing *E. salicis* from non-pathogens. He thought pectin degradation by *E. salicis* (but not by saprophytes) a useful characteristic. This is most usually so in *E. salicis* (Buchanan and Gibbons, 1974) but may not occur in some strains (see below). Lindeijer (1932) described watermark disease in the Netherlands. More recently, Gremmen and De Kam (1970) have shown that *E. salicis* is the organism involved there, clearing up the notion of Lindeijer that this disease was caused by a *Pseudomonad*. Lindeijer also thought *E. salicis* was indole positive, but all the evidence from Wong (1974), Gremmen and De Kam (1970), De Kam (1976), and as listed in Buchanan and Gibbons (1974), is that *E. salicis* is indole negative. Lindeijer first noted that her isolates were all unable to produce yellow pigment on potato plugs. Some strains examined from Essex, UK, produce yellow pigment, others do not. Dutch isolates more recently examined by De Kam do not produce yellow pigment on potato media. Yellow pigment production (contrary to Buchanan and Gibbons, 1974) is not a reliable characteristic.

Wong (1974) noted differences in sensitivity to N.C.P.P.B. 1466 phage, and to a lesser extent in agglutination reactions and liquefaction of pectate gel media. More recently, De Kam (1976) reports that English isolates will grow in a medium using $D(+)$ galactose as sole carbon source, whereas Dutch isolates will not. It seems too, that all the Dutch isolates tested by him (none of which produced yellow pigment on potato media) would not grow in a medium containing raffinose as the sole carbon source. Using 3 isolates of *E. salicis* made by Dowson (N.C.P.P.B. 447, 1466 and I.C.P.P. E.S.4) Dye (1968) could detect no reduction of nitrate to nitrate as observed by Dowson (1937). As listed in Buchanan and Gibbons (1974), Wong, together with Gremmen and De Kam, reported nitrate reduction in all strains of *E. salicis* tested.

Characteristics of Isolates of *Erwinia salicis* from Essex, UK, 1971-1973

Methods used were those described by Cruickshank *et al.* (1970), and in addition, litmus milk (Dowson, 1957); oxidase (Kovacs, 1956); pectic enzymes (Hildebrand, 1971); oxidative–fermentative metabolism test

(Hugh and Leifson, 1953) and gelatin hydrolysis (Harrigan and Mc-Chance, 1966). Potato plugs were made by putting pieces of potato in test tubes on absorbent cotton wool and adding 2% aqueous glycerol to the base of the plug. Pathogenicity means blackening in the detached shoot test described above. Agglutination means a positive slide test using antiserum produced as described above to *E. salicis* N.C.P.P.B. 1466. The phage tests were kindly performed by R. A. Lelliott using a phage isolated by him from *E. salicis* N.C.P.P.B. 1466. The isolates we discuss here were all isolated from trees showing the watermark symptom felled in East Anglia, UK, 1971–1973, and are compared in Table 2. Isolates 34, 35 and 36 were from the same tree of *S. caprea* (goat willow) at Langham. Isolate 40 was from a single tree of *S. vitellina* in Suffolk. All other isolates were from *S. alba* var. *caerulea* and were obtained as follows: 7, 8, 14 a single tree at Writtle; 32, 33 likewise a single tree at Bulmer; 22, 23 a single tree at Coggeshall; 42 at Little Baddow; 43 at Wooden Walter.

As can be seen in Table 2 the variable results concern the production of yellow pigment, phage sensitivity, agglutination and pectate gel liquefaction. Two of these variations (agglutination weak, pectate gel not liquefied) were confined to Leeds isolates 33 and 34, which, although isolated from different species of *Salix*, in different places, (see above) were similar to each other. They were also phage negative, and seem to be different from the other isolates. Isolate 33, however, produced yellow pigment on potato plugs, and 34 did not.

In addition to 34, yellow pigment was not produced on potato plugs by 7, 32 and 23. Only two isolates (8, 14) other than N.C.P.P.B. 1466 produced any detectable pigment at all on nutrient agar. All isolates (except 8) lost their ability to produce yellow pigment on potato plugs after prolonged subculturing on GNA. It is of interest in this connection that Lakso and Starr (1970) classified *E. salicis* as a "phytopathogenic, true, *Erwinia* sp., (*white* colony)" to distinguish it from *E. milletiae* which they describe as a "phytopathogenic, true, *Erwinia* sp. (yellow colony)".

Isolates 33, 34, 36 and 40 were negative to N.C.P.P.B. 1466 phage. These four phage negative isolates gave strongly positive agglutination with the N.C.P.P.B. 1466 antiserum. It is now clear that strains of *E. salicis* exist with differing characteristics, sometimes in the same diseased tree.

The problem of Dye (1968, 1969), detecting neither reduction of nitrate, nor pectate activity in a pectate gel medium is difficult to understand. Our experience is that we have isolated only two strains (33, 34) which did not liquefy pectate gel. It is characteristic of *E. salicis*. Like-

TABLE 2. Certain characteristics of isolates of *Erwinia salicis* obtained from *Salix* spp. with watermark disease in East Anglia, UK, 1971–1973

Leeds isolate No.	7	8	14	32	33	34	35	36	22	23	40	42	43	N.C.P.P.B. 1466	Bergey (1975)
Oxidase	−	−	−	−	−	−	−	−	−	−	−	−	−	−	−
Starch hydrolysis	−	−	−	−	−	−	−	−	−	−	−	−	−	−	n.s.
Gelatin	−	−	−	−	−	−	−	−	−	−	−	−	−	−	−
Indole	−	−	−	−	−	−	−	−	−	−	−	−	−	−	−
Litmus milk	−	−	−	−	−	−	−	−	−	−	−	−	−	−	−
Methyl Red	−	−	−	−	−	−	−	−	−	−	−	−	−	−	−
Nitrate reduction	+	+	+	+	+	+	+	+	+	+	+	+	+	+	+
Voges-Proskauer	+	+	+	+	+	+	+	+	+	+	+	+	+	+	+
OF Metabolism	F	F	F	F	F	F	F	F	F	F	F	F	F	F	F
Yellow on potato plug	−	+	+	−	+	−	+	+	+	−	+	+	+	+	+
Yellow on N.A.	−	+	+	+	±	±	+	−	+	+	+	−	−	+	+
Agglutination	n.t.	+	+	+	−	−	+	+	+	+	+	+	+	+	n.s.
'phage	n.t.	+	+	+	−	−	+	+	+	+	−	−	+	+	n.s.
Pectate gel	+	+	+	+	−	+	+	+	+	+	+	+	+	+	+
Pathogenicity	+	+	+	+	+	+	+	+	+	+	+	+	+	+	+

n.t., not tested.
n.s., not specified.

wise we have never isolated a strain which did not reduce nitrate to nitrite. It may be that Dye's pectate gel was too acid (pH 6·4). We find all strains of *E. salicis* fail to liquefy pectate gel if the pH is below 7·0. Pectinase activity is much stronger in alkaline media, perhaps near 9·0 being the optimal pH. (Lakso and Starr, 1970, also thought *E. salicis* did not liquefy pectate with N.C.P.P.B. 1466.)

References

ADEGEYE, A. O. (1975). A study of *Erwinia salicis* infections following artificial inoculation of *Salix alba* var. *caerulea*. M. Phil. Thesis, University of Leeds.

ANONYMOUS (1974). *The Watermark Disease (Local Authorities) Order 1974.* Statutory Instrument No. 768, Plant health. London: HMSO.

BILLING, EVE, CROSSE, J. E. & GARRETT, C. M. E. (1960). Laboratory diagnosis of fire blight and bacterial blossom blight of pear. *Plant Pathology*, **9**, 19–25.

BUCHANAN, R. E. & GIBBONS, N. E. (1974) (eds). *Bergey's manual of determinative bacteriology* 8th edn. Baltimore: Williams and Wilkins.

CALLOW, J. A. & LING, IRENE T. (1973). Histology of neoplasms and chlorotic lesions in maize seedlings following the injection of sporidia of *Ustilago maydis* (DC) Corda. *Physiological Plant Pathology*, **3**, 489–494.

CONN, H. J. & LILLIE, R. D. (1969). *Conn's biological stains* 8th edn. Baltimore: Williams and Wilkins.

CRUICKSHANK, R., DUGUID, J. P. & SWAIN, R. H. A. (1970). *Medical microbiology* 11th edn. Edinburgh and London: Livingstone.

DAY, W. R. (1924). The watermark disease of the cricket bat willow (*Salix caerulea*). *Oxford forestry memoirs* No. 3. Oxford: Oxford University Press.

DE KAM, M. (1976). *Erwinia salicis*: its metabolism and variability *in vitro*, and a method to demonstrate the pathogen in the host. *Antonie van Leeuwenhoek*, **42**, 421–428.

DOWSON, W. J. (1937). *Bacterium salicis* Day. The cause of the watermark disease of the cricket bat willow. *Annals of Applied Biology* **24**, 528–544.

DOWSON, W. J. (1957). *Plant diseases due to bacteria* 2nd edn. Cambridge: Cambridge University Press.

DYE, D. W. (1968). A taxonomic study of the genus *Erwinia*. I. The "amylovora" group. *New Zealand Journal of Science*, **12**, 81–97.

DYE, D. W. (1969). A taxonomic study of the genus *Erwinia*. III. The "herbicola" group. *New Zealand Journal of Science*, **12**, 223–236.

FEDER, N. & O'BRIEN, T. P. (1968). Plant microtechnique. Some principles and new methods. *American Journal of Botany*, **55**, 123–142.

GEORGALA, D. L. & BOOTHROYD, M. (1968). Immunofluorescence—a useful technique for microbial identification. In *Identification methods for microbiologists* (Gibbs, B. M. and Shapton, D. A., eds.). Soc. appl. bact. Tech. Series No. 2. London and New York: Academic Press, p. 187.

GHEMAWAT, M. S. (1977). Polychromatic staining with toluidine blue O for studying host-parasite relationships in wheat mildew. *Physiological Plant Pathology*, **11**, 251–253.

GRAHAM, D. C. (1963). Serological diagnosis of potato black-leg and tuber soft rot. *Plant Pathology*, **12**, 142–144.

GREMMEN, J. & DE KAM, L. (1970). *Erwinia salicis* as the cause of dieback in *Salix alba* in the Netherlands and its identity with *Pseudomonas saliciperda*. *Netherlands Journal of Plant Pathology*, **76**, 249–252.

HARRIGAN, W. F. & MCCHANCE, M. E. (1966). *Laboratory methods in microbiology*. London and New York: Academic Press.

HILDEBRAND, D. C. (1971). Pectate and pectin gels for differentiation of *Pseudomonas* sp. and other plant pathogenic bacteria. *Phytopathology*, **61**, 1430–1436.

HOEFERT, L. L. (1968). Polychromatic stains for thin sections of *Beta* embedded in epoxy resin. *Stain Technology*, **43**, 145–151.

HUGH, R. & LEIFSON, E. (1953). The taxonomic significance of fermentative versus oxidative metabolism of carbohydrate by various Gram negative bacteria. *Journal of Bacteriology*, **66**, 24–26.

KOVACS, N. (1956). Identification of *Pseudomonas pyocyanea* by the oxidase reaction. *Nature, London*, **178**, 703.

LAKSO, J. U. & STARR, M. P. (1970). Comparative injuriousness to plants of *Erwinia* spp. and other Enterobacteria from plants and animals. *Journal of Applied Bacteriology*, **33**, 692–707.

LINDEIJER, E. J. (1932). The bacterial disease of willow caused by *Pseudomonas saliciperda* n.sp. Doctoral Thesis, University of Amsterdam.

MARKS, G. E. (1965). The cytology of *Phytophthora infestans*. *Chromosoma*, **16**, 681–692.

MARKS, G. E. (1973). A rapid HCl/Toluidine blue squash technic for plant chromosomes. *Stain Technology*, **48**, 229–231.

MEENAKSHI, G., SOLOMON, J. J. & SULOCHANA, C. B. (1972). Toluidine blue metachromasia; A means for early detection of plant virus infection *Stain Technology*, **47**, 267–268.

METCALFE, G. (1940). The watermark disease of willows. I. Host-parasite relationships. *New Phytologist*, **39**, 322–332.

MOATS, W. A. (1961). Chemical changes in bacteria heated in milk as related to loss of stainability. *Journal of Dairy Science*, **44**, 1431–1439.

O'BRIEN, T. P., FEDER, N. & MCCULLY, M. E. (1964). Polychromatic staining of plant cell walls by toluidine blue O. *Protoplasma*, **59**, 368–373.

PREECE, T. F. (1971a). Fluorescent techniques in mycology. In *Methods in microbiology*, vol. 4 (Booth, C., ed.). London and New York: Academic Press, p. 509.

PREECE, T. F. (1971b). Immunological techniques in mycology. In *Methods in microbiology*, vol. 4 (Booth, C., ed.). London and New York: Academic Press, 599.

PREECE, T. F. (1977). *Watermark disease of the cricket bat willow*. Forestry Commission Leaflet No. 20. London: HMSO.

PREECE, T. F. & COOPER, D. J. (1969). The preparation and use of a fluorescent antibody reagent for *Botrytis cinerea* grown on glass slides. *Transactions of the British Mycological Society*, **52**, 99–104.

PURVIS, M. J., COLLIER, D. C. & WALLS, D. (1966). *Laboratory techniques in Botany*. London: Butterworths.

SAKAI, W. S. (1973). Simple method for differential staining of paraffin embedded plant material using toluidine blue O. *Stain Technology*, **48**, 247–249.

SHARON, E. M. (1973). Some histological features of *Acer saccharum* wood formed after wounding. *Canadian Journal of Forest Research*, **3**, 83–89.

SHOEMAKER, R. A. & RIDDELL, R. T. (1954). Staining *Streptomyces scabies* in lesions of common scab of potato. *Stain Technology*, **29**, 59–61.

SIDMAN, R. L., MOTTLA, P. A. & FEDER, N. (1961). Improved polyester wax embedding for histology. *Stain Technology*, **36**, 279–284.

STECHER, P. G., FINKEL, M. J. & SEIGMUND, Q. H. (1968) (eds). *The Merck index of chemicals and drugs* 8th edn. New York: Merck and Co.

STOUGHTON, R. H. (1930). Thionin and Orange G for the differential staining of bacteria and fungi in plant tissue. *Annals of Applied Biology*, **17**, 162–164.

TOWNSEND, G. F. (1957). An alkaline hyrolysis toluidine blue method applied to growing yeast cells. *Stain Technology*, **32**, 302–303.

WALKER, P. D., BATTY, IRENE, & THOMAS, R. O. (1971). The localization of bacterial antigens by the use of the fluorescent and ferritin labelled antibody techniques. In *Methods in microbiology*, vol. 5A (Norris, J. R. & Ribbons, D. W., eds). London and New York: Academic Press, p. 219.

WONG, W. C. (1974). Watermark disease of cricket bat willow: Epidemiology and the nature of the symptoms in the wood. Ph.D. Thesis, The University of Leeds.

WONG, W. C. & PREECE, T. F. (1973). Infection of cricket bat willow (*Salix alba* var. *caerulea* Sm.) by *Erwinia salicis* (Day) Chester detected in the field by the use of a specific antiserum. *Plant Pathology*, **22**, 96–97.

Bacterial Soft-rot of Potatoes

BARBARA M. LUND

ARC Food Research Institute, Colney Lane, Norwich, Norfolk, England

Bacterial soft-rot is one of the most important causes of microbial spoilage of potatoes and one of the few diseases that can spread extensively through a store. The spoilage is due mainly to *Erwinia carotovora*, an organism which is also responsible for post-harvest deterioration of a wide range of vegetables (Lund, 1971). During storage potatoes are also liable to spoilage caused by various fungal diseases. A review of the effect of field and storage factors on bacterial soft-rot and other storage diseases of potatoes was published by Boyd (1972).

About 5 million tonnes of potatoes are grown annually in Great Britain for human consumption. After harvesting, a high proportion of these potatoes, apart from early varieties, are stored for up to 8 months in bulk or in $\frac{1}{2}$ or 1 tonne pallet boxes in stores with capacities of up to 1000 tonnes. As soon as the tubers have been loaded into store (Fig. 1), ventilation is often restricted to allow the humidity to increase and the temperature to rise to about 13–15° (55–59°F). This temperature, coupled with high humidity, should be maintained for a period of about 2 weeks (the so-called "curing" period) to promote healing of wounds caused during harvesting and handling, and thus to reduce subsequent deterioration due to diseases such as gangrene and skinspot (caused respectively by *Phoma exigua* var. *foveata* and *Oospora pustulans*) and to reduce moisture loss. However, the conditions required for wound-healing favour infection by soft-rot bacteria and if the crop is thought to be liable to such infection it may be necessary to omit the curing period (Burton, 1963, 1966; MAFF, 1972). After this initial curing the temperature in a store is reduced to that required for long-term storage. The temperature is controlled by ventilation either by convection, or by forced draught or by re-circulation using either ambient or refrigerated air (Burton, 1963, 1966; MAFF, 1972).

It is usually desirable to store potatoes at a high relative humidity and at temperatures between 5 and 10°. If the tubers are stored for processing,

FIG. 1. Potatoes in a 500 tonne potato store (published by permission of the Potato Marketing Board).

particularly for manufacture of crisps, it is general practice to prevent the temperature from falling below 7° in order to minimize sweetening, since a high content of reducing sugars leads to unacceptable darkening of crisps. At temperatures above 3·5–4·5° sprouting can occur, and this is prevented by treatment with a chemical sprout suppressant (Burton, 1966). Compounds which have been cleared under the Pesticides Safety Precautions Scheme for use as sprout suppressants include tecnazene (tetrachloronitrobenzene, TCNB), propham (isopropyl N-phenylcarbamate, IPC) chlorpropham (isopropyl N-(3-chlorophenyl) carbamate, CIPC) and nonanol (3,5,5-trimethylhexan-1-ol). Formulations of the first three of these compounds have been approved by the Agricultural

PLATE 1. Potato plants showing symptoms of blackleg. (a) Young plants showing yellowing and rolling of leaves. (b) A single infected plant in a healthy crop. (c) and (d) Infected mature plants showing characteristic blackening at the base of the stem. Plates 1(a) and (c) reproduced by permission of Dr. D. C. Graham, Department of Agriculture for Scotland. Plate 1(d) reproduced by permission of Dr. R. Goth, USDA, ARS, Beltsville, Maryland, USA.

(a)

(b)

(c)

(d)

Chemicals Approval Scheme. Tecnazene is usually applied as a dust or in the form of granules when potatoes are loaded into store. Chlorpropham alone or as a mixture with propham can be applied as a vapour twice during a medium-term storage season, or may be used as delayed-release granules applied when the tubers are loaded into store, and intended to retard the release of the active ingredient until wound-healing is complete. Nonanol can be applied intermittently as a vapour (Burton, 1966). Compounds which have been cleared and approved for use as fungicides on stored potatoes include tecnazene (already referred to as a sprout suppressant) and thiabendazole (2-thiazol-4-yl) benzimidazole, which is usually applied in a coarse spray or as an ultra-low-volume mist to potatoes as they are loaded into store.

There are few records showing the extent of losses resulting from bacterial soft-rot in storage and in transit. During 1961–1962 in a survey of 41 farms storing potatoes in buildings the average loss due to rot was estimated at 15% by weight, with a range of 2% to 68% on individual farms (Twiss and Jones, 1965); rots due to blight (*Phytophthora infestans*) and gangrene were probably included in this estimate. In a survey by the Potato Marketing Board in collaboration with Rothamsted Experimental Station covering 571 farms in 1966 and 751 farms in 1967 the average incidence of rots was about 5% in both years (Church *et al.*, 1970). During the 1974–1975 and 1976–1977 seasons in the UK many loads of wet and dirty potatoes had to be put into stores after lifting in cold, wet conditions and losses due to soft rot may have exceeded 5%.

On the basis of a loss of 3% of a total crop of 4·5 million tonnes with a wholesale price of £60 per tonne, the cost of the loss due to bacterial soft-rot would be about £8 million. In fact, in 1976–1977 drought during the growing season and wet conditions at harvest, with consequent difficulty in harvesting, resulted in a low yield and abnormally high wholesale prices of up to £200 per tonne in January 1977. Losses due to bacterial soft-rot in Wisconsin, USA, during storage and transport were estimated recently as about 3% (De Boer, 1976).

Bacteria Which Cause Soft-rot

Erwinia carotovora

The bacteria which are the main cause of soft-rot of potatoes are *Erwinia carotovora* var. *atroseptica* and *E. carotovora* var. *carotovora* (Lelliott, 1974). When the variety involved was not identified or when both may have been involved, the name *E. carotovora* is used in this paper without specifying the variety. Anaerogenic strains of *E. carotovora*, previously called *E. aroideae* or *E. carotovora* var. *aroideae* are now regarded as strains of *E. carotovora* var. *carotovora* (Lelliott, 1974). *Erwinia carotovora* var. *atroseptica* is usually the cause of blackleg of potatoes (Plate 1) in the field in temperate climates (Graham and Harper, 1967; Lapwood and Hide, 1971) but strains of var. *carotovora* have been reported as a cause of the disease in Arizona (Stanghellini and Meneley, 1975) and in Japan (Tani and Akai, 1975). *Erwinia carotovora* var. *carotovora* was reported to cause rotting of stem-tops and petioles of potato plants in India (Shekhawat *et al.*, 1976) and was found in rotting stems in the field in Scotland (Graham *et al.*, 1976).

Isolations from rotting tubers and from blackleg in Scotland showed that 15 to 17% of the *E. carotovora* isolates were var. *carotovora* and 83 to 87% were var. *atroseptica* (Malcolmson, 1959; Pérombelon, 1968, 1972). A similar proportion of var. *atroseptica* was found in isolations from healthy tubers (Pérombelon, 1973). Roumanian workers reported that 84% of isolations from stems in the field were var. *atroseptica* and 16% were var. *carotovora* whereas 90% of isolates from stored potatoes were var. *carotovora* (Lazar and Bucur, 1964).

The question of the major source of the blackleg organism has been the subject of controversy (discussed by De Boer, 1976). When these bacteria are introduced into soil the numbers decrease over a period of weeks to levels which cannot readily be detected and many workers have concluded that the organisms do not survive over winter in soil (Ramsey, 1919; Graham, 1958; Voronkevitch and Butsevich, 1964; Lazar and Bucur, 1964; Graham and Harper, 1967; Logan, 1968). Other workers have concluded that these bacteria can survive the winter in soil in certain conditions (Leach, 1930, 1931; Bonde, 1950; Van den Boom, 1967) and survival is improved in the presence of plant debris (Logan, 1968; Ficke, *et al.*, 1973). Volunteer plants ("ground-keepers") may also harbour the organism and *E. carotovora* var. *atroseptica* and var. *carotovora* could be detected in association with tubers produced by volunteers growing in barley 4 years after the previous potato crop (Pérombelon and Lowe, 1971). *Erwinia carotovora* survives in the lenticels of stored tubers, and thus the seed potato is a major source of the bacterium (Graham and Hardie, 1971; Perombelon, 1972, 1973; De Boer, 1976). After planting, when the plant is established, decay of the mother tuber (or the seed piece) is accompanied by multiplication of *E. carotovora* which can be detected in the rhizosphere of potato plants during the growing season (De Boer *et al.*, 1974; De Boer, 1976) and, depending on soil moisture, can move through the soil and infect daughter tubers (Graham, 1962; Graham and Harper, 1967; Pérombelon, 1974, 1976; De Boer, 1976). There is some evidence that *E. carotovora* survives in the rhizosphere of other crops, particularly Chinese cabbage and other cruciferous plants (Kikumoto and Sakamoto, 1969a, 1969b; Togashi, 1972; Voronkevitch *et al.*, 1972; Kikumoto, 1974; Mew *et al.*, 1976) and can be isolated from fields where fennel has previously been grown (Mazzucchi and Dalli, 1974). The organism can cause spoilage of these crops in the field and has also been recovered from the rhizosphere of cotton plants (Klingner *et al.*, 1971).

Following recognition of the fact that the seed potato is a major source of overwintering disease organisms, particularly *E. carotovora* var. *atroseptica*, the propagation of potato stocks from tested stem cuttings has been undertaken by the Department of Agriculture and Fisheries for Scotland (DAFS) to produce seed potatoes free from *E. carotovora* and other disease or spoilage organisms (Graham and Hardie, 1971). To avoid re-infection of the stocks the DAFS raises and multiplies the nuclear tubers (progeny from stem cuttings) on an upland farm where no commercial crops are grown, and under strictly hygienic conditions. Material propagated clonally by the DAFS for up to 3 years from stem cuttings forms the nuclear "VTSC" (Virus-tested Stem Cutting) stocks. Nuclear clones from the DAFS farm are released to commercial VTSC growers for further multiplication for up to 5 years, and the progeny constitutes the highest grade in the Scottish Seed Potato Certification Scheme. The VTSC growers, in turn, pass this produce to growers of lower grades, and ultimately all seed potato stocks in Scotland will be derived from VTSC material. During propagation of tubers on the nuclear stock farm, a small amount of re-infection has occurred, mainly by *E. carotovora* var. *carotovora* (Graham *et al.*, 1976). The organism was probably transmitted by insects, and perhaps also by birds and on machinery; in potato-growing areas bacterial aerosols may also be an important means of dissemination (Graham and Harrison, 1975). A survey in 1973–1974 and 1974–1975 showed the occurrence of re-contamination by var. *carotovora* and to a lesser extent by var. *atroseptica* during multiplication of these stocks by commercial VTSC growers (Pérombelon *et al.*, 1976). Further surveys indicate that, more recently, the level of recontamination has decreased (D. C. Graham, pers. comm.). If this recontamination can be kept down to a low level, the continual replacement of infected seed stocks by VTSC material should reduce the risk of blackleg and the general level of *E. carotovora* and of spoilage fungi associated with tubers.

Pectolytic clostridia

The occurrence of starch-degrading, pectolytic clostridia in potatoes rotting in clamps was reported by Rudd Jones and Dowson (1950), and

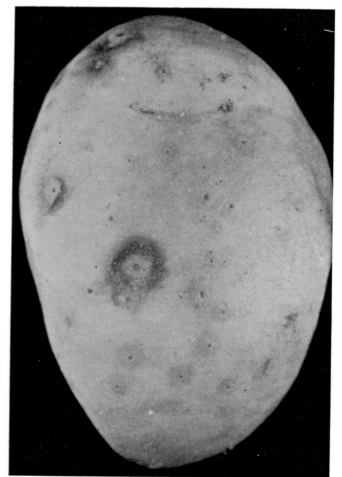

FIG. 2.

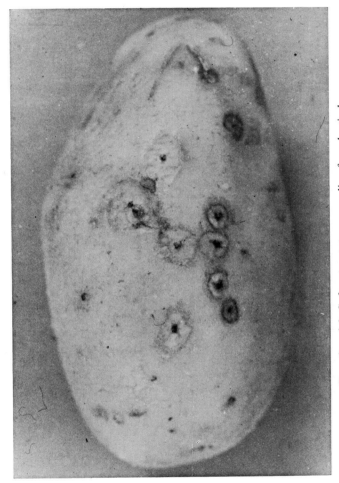

FIGS 2 and 3. Soft-rot potatoes spreading from lenticels.

inoculation of tubers with a mixture of *E. carotovora* and a *Clostridium* sp. caused more extensive rotting at 25° than that due to *E. carotovora* alone. Pectolytic clostridia have since been isolated consistently from tubers induced to rot in anaerobic conditions (Lund and Nicholls, 1970; Lund and Wyatt, 1972) or by incubation in a mist chamber (Lund and Kelman, 1977). The main habitat of these clostridia is probably the soil, but there is a lack of information regarding the numbers and distribution of pectolytic clostridia; however they can usually be isolated from potatoes by enrichment methods. From experiments in which bacteria were injected into whole tubers which were then incubated in anaerobic conditions, Pérombelon *et al.* (1977) concluded that 2 strains of pectolytic clostridia were as virulent as strains of *E. carotovora* at 22°, but considerably less so at 16°. However, there is some evidence (M.C.M. Pérombelon, pers. comm.) that other strains of pectolytic clostridia may be more active than the above strains at 16°.

Other pectolytic bacteria

Other pectolytic bacteria, for example species of *Pseudomonas* (Rudd-Jones and Dowson, 1950; Sampson and Hayward, 1971; Lapwood and Legg, 1972), *Flavobacterium* (Sampson and Hayward, 1971) and of *Bacillus* (Dowson, 1943, 1944; Jackson and Henry, 1946), are often associated with the surface of tubers. The frequency of isolation of these bacteria from the leading edge of rotting tissue in potatoes is relatively low compared with that of *E. carotovora* and pectolytic clostridia. Strains of *Pseudomonas marginalis*, *P. syringae* and *Flavobacterium* sp. were reported only to be weakly pathogenic to potato tubers, possibly because their rate of formation of macerating enzymes was relatively slow compared with that of *E. carotovora* (Lapwood, 1957; Murant and Wood, 1957a, 1957b). Rotting due to *Bacillus* spp. is probably only important at relatively high temperatures (>30°, Dowson, 1943; Jackson and Henry, 1946).

Factors Leading to Bacterial Spoilage

Rotting of potatoes infected by soft-rot bacteria can be initiated from lenticels (Smith and Ramsey, 1947; Bétencourt and Prunier, 1965; Fox *et al.*, 1971; Adams, 1975; Pérombelon and Lowe, 1975) (Figs 2 and 3), from wounds (Leach, 1930; Smith, 1950; Smith and Smart, 1955; Harper *et al.*, 1963; Scholey *et al.*, 1968; Fox *et al.*, 1971) or from the point of attachment of the stolon (Graham and Harper, 1967) (Figs 4 and 5). The spoilage frequently takes the form of a soft, white rot which

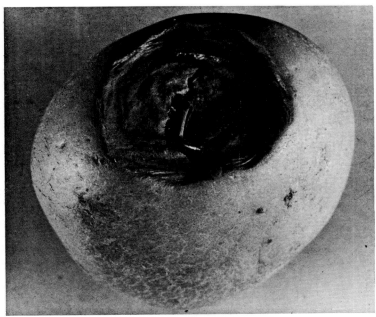

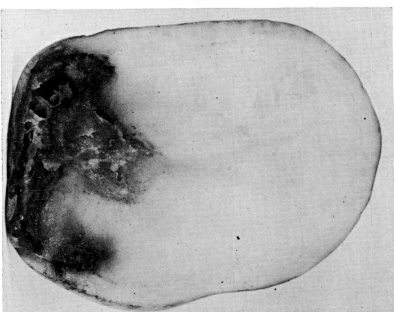

FIGS 4 and 5. Soft-rot of potato tubers spreading from the point of attachment of the stolon. (Supplied by Dr. D. C. Graham.)

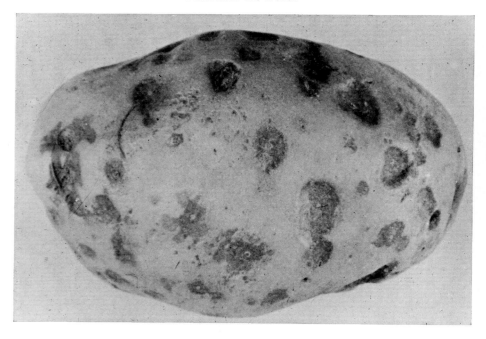

FIG. 6. "Bacterial hard rot" of a potato tuber. Rotting initiated from lenticels has been arrested by dry conditions.

can spread rapidly throughout the tuber. The name "bacterial hard rot" has been used to describe the dry, brown, necrotic lesions which can result when rotting initiated from lenticels or from wounds is restricted in dry conditions (Logan, 1964) (Fig. 6). Rotting can also follow damage by frost, sun-scald or infection by other diseases, particularly late blight, gangrene and dry rot, *Fusarium solani* var. *caeruleum* (Dowson and Rudd-Jones, 1951; Boyd, 1972). The initiation of rotting may be influenced by field factors such as the application of a high level of fertilizer (Boyd, 1972), growth in wet soil conditions and the infection of a high proportion of plants with blackleg, but is largely determined by the environmental factors during storage or transit including the temperature, relative humidity (RH), the presence of free moisture and the composition of the gaseous atmosphere (Ruehle, 1940; Ramsey *et al.*, 1944; Nielsen, 1968; Cromarty and Easton, 1973; Naumann *et al.*, 1976). In the range 7 to 20° and at approximately 100% RH the incidence of rotting increases with increase in storage temperature (Kendrick *et al.*, 1959) but at 90–100% RH rotting due to *E. carotovora* var. *atroseptica* and to var. *carotovora* has been reported at temperatures as low as 4° (Hingorani and Addy, 1953). Major factors leading to soft-rot are the presence of surface water on tubers and depletion of oxygen within tubers (Lund and Nicholls, 1970; Lund and Wyatt, 1972; Pérombelon and Lowe, 1975; De Boer, 1976) (Fig. 7). This depletion may be due to the effect of high temperature (Burton, 1950), resulting in an increase in metabolic rate and oxygen demand of the tuber, to restricted aeration during transport in closed containers (Nielsen, 1968) or to the presence of a film of water on tubers, decreasing the rate of diffusion of air into tubers through the lenticels (Burton and Wigginton, 1970; Wigginton, 1973). The liability of wet tubers to rot is well known (Smith and Ramsey, 1947; Burton, 1963); in practice adequate drying of washed tubers is essential and was the major factor leading to control of most bacterial soft-rot of potatoes in transit from Florida (Ruehle, 1940).

Different batches of tubers differ in their predisposition to decay. Factors likely to cause such differences are the numbers of soft-rotting bacteria initially present, the maturity and physiological condition of the tubers and the degree of mechanical damage. In view of the quantities of potatoes which are stored, it would be of value if stocks of tubers with poor storage potential could be identified before storage. Zielke et al. (1974) claimed that a correlation existed between the appearance of blackleg in a crop in July and subsequent development of soft-rot in store. It was suggested that a single screening of growing crops in July might therefore identify high-risk crops which should receive minimal storage. In collaborative work between Rothamsted Experimental Station and the Potato Marketing Board Experimental Station no correlation was found between the extent of blackleg in the field and the incidence of latent E. carotovora on tubers in August, and development of soft-rot during subsequent storage (Potato Marketing Board, 1975).

A convenient method has been described for evaluating the soft-rot potential of tubers at the time of sampling (Lund and Kelman, 1977); this technique, which involves incubation of tubers in a mist chamber, should prove useful for evaluating factors affecting the predisposition of potatoes to soft-rot.

Control of Spoilage

From the preceding discussion it is clear that in order to prevent soft-rot it is important to avoid storing wet tubers, to control storage conditions, in particular to prevent formation of condensation on the tubers (Ferguson, 1969; MAFF, 1972) and to ensure that washed tubers are thoroughly dried before transport (Ruehle, 1940). It is also important

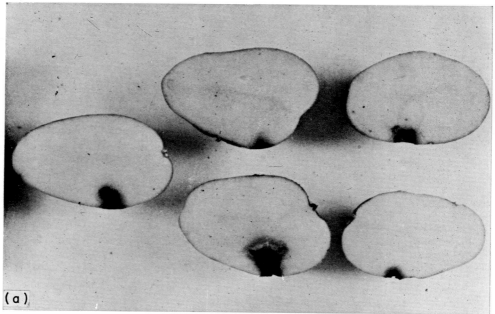

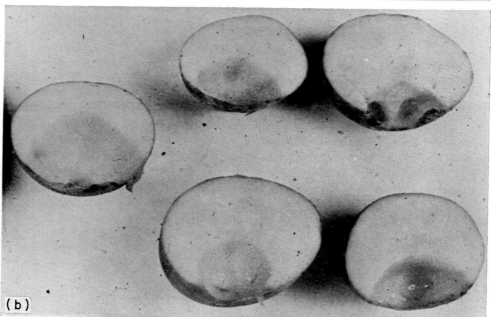

FIG. 7. The effect of depletion of oxygen on susceptibility of potatoes to bacterial soft-rot. King Edward tubers wounded and inoculated with *E. carotovora* var. *atroseptica* and stored for 16 days at 10° and 100% relative humidity (a) in air (b) in 1% O_2 + 99% N_2.

not to store potatoes which are immature, or which have suffered damage due to frost or exposure to strong sunlight, or which are showing signs of rot or infection with fungal diseases. Attempts to reduce the numbers of *E. carotovora* on the tubers by use of good quality seed and good crop management, and care to minimize damage during harvesting and handling (Potato Marketing Board, 1974; Smittle *et al.*, 1974), are clearly measures which reduce the risk of spoilage. During a wet season it may be difficult to avoid placing wet tubers in store. In this situation it is generally advisable to omit the curing period, reduce the temperature as soon as possible and attempt to dry the crop by ventilation (MAFF, 1972).

At present there appear to be few chemicals available which will destroy bacteria within plant tissue and it may be difficult to eliminate soft-rot entirely by this means. Attempts have been made to reduce the incidence of soft-rot by addition of chlorine to wash-water. Treatment of washed potatoes with 500 mg litre^{-1} of chlorine in the presence of a biodegradable detergent was reported to reduce lenticel infection of washed potatoes (Wilson and Johnston, 1967). Scholey *et al.* (1968) found that while addition of 2000 mg litre^{-1} of available chlorine to wash-water contaminated with *E. carotovora* reduced the number of rots developing in the first 2 days after packaging, there was an increase in the number of rots which developed after 16 days. In general it has been found that chlorine solutions do not prevent decay of vegetables which have become inoculated prior to treatment, but use of chlorine in washing or hydro-cooling of vegetables can give an important benefit by preventing build-up in the wash-water of an inoculum of soft-rot bacteria (Thompson, 1969).

In laboratory experiments Bonde (1953) found that streptomycin sulphate (10 mg litre^{-1}) prevented decay of potato slices inoculated with *E. carotovora*. However, the difficulty of obtaining disinfection of naturally-infected, whole tubers may be inferred from the fact that treatment of seed potatoes with streptomycin (200 mg litre^{-1}) failed to prevent development of blackleg after planting (Graham and Volcani, 1961). Even if effective, treatment of potatoes with medically important antibiotics is unlikely to be acceptable. Antibacterials which have been cleared under the Pesticides Safety Precautions Scheme for use on stored potatoes include dichlorophen and an iodophor (nonylphenoxy poly(ethylenoxy)ethanol iodine complex), but so far there is little evidence that treatment with these compounds reduces soft-rot.

Isolation and Properties of *Erwinia carotovora*

Media and methods of isolation

In order to isolate and enumerate *E. carotovora* from soils, methods which involve preparation of dilutions from soil samples, followed by plating on selective media usually detect the organism only in concentrations of 10^2 or 10^3 g^{-1} dry weight of soil (Logan, 1968; Togashi, 1972; Cuppels and Kelman, 1974). Greater sensitivity may be achieved by a quantal method of counting (Pérombelon, 1971a), by concentration of samples on membrane filters (Mazzucchi and Dalli, 1974) or by enrichment in a liquid medium (Meneley and Stanghellini, 1976) followed by isolation on an appropriate solid medium. Methods involving the use of potato or carrot tissue as an enrichment medium followed by plating on selective media have been used to isolate low numbers of soft-rotting bacteria from soil (Leach, 1931; Kerr, 1953; Graham, 1958; Kikumoto and Sakamoto, 1967; Togashi, 1972; De Boer, 1976). Checks are necessary to ensure that the plant tissue itself is not the source of the bacteria. Carrot slices used in this way should be incubated at 20° rather than 30° to avoid enrichment for *Bacillus polymyxa* (Togashi, 1972). There is little information on the sensitivity of the latter enrichment methods, and it will clearly depend on the actual technique used.

Several selective media, listed by Cuppels and Kelman (1974) and O'Neill and Logan (1975), have been developed for isolating *E. carotovora* from soil and plant tissue. The media of Logan (1963) and Stewart (1962) have been widely used and consist of Simmons Citrate agar and MacConkey agar respectively, with an over-layer of pectate gel. On these media colonies of *E. carotovora* grow in the centre of characteristic depressions due to degradation of the pectate, and with experience can usually be distinguished from colonies of other pectolytic bacteria (Fig. 8). According to Pérombelon (1971b) the bile salts in Stewart's medium had some toxic effect on *E. carotovora* and substitution by 20 mg litre^{-1} of a non-toxic anionic surface-active agent (Agral 90, Plant Protection Ltd) resulted in an increase of up to 50% in counts. These three media are useful for isolation of *E. carotovora* after enrichment in a suitable medium or in plant tissue. Cuppels and Kelman's (1974) single-layer, pectate medium was considerably more selective than the above media, particularly when modified by the incorporation of manganous sulphate in a concentration of 0·8 g litre^{-1} MnSO$_4$ (O'Neill and Logan, 1975). Production of foam during preparation can be overcome by addition of an antifoam agent (O'Neill and Logan, 1975), but the medium

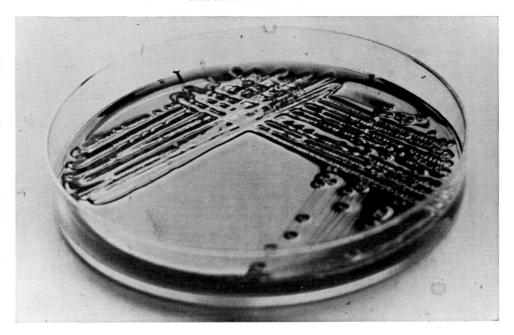

Fig. 8. Colonies of *E. carotovora* var. *atroseptica* on Stewart's pectate medium after incubation for 2 days at 25°.

has to be poured into plates immediately after autoclaving, since it solidifies rapidly and cannot be re-melted. By examination under oblique light colonies of *E. carotovora* on Cuppels and Kelman's medium appear irridiscent, translucent and criss-crossed with internal markings and can usually be differentiated by the experienced worker from those of other pectolytic bacteria. Logan's medium becomes toxic to *E. carotovora* during storage, (O'Neill and Logan, 1975) resulting in low recovery rates, and the possibility of such an effect should be recognized in the use of selective media.

Physiological, biochemical and serological properties

The properties of the genus *Erwinia* have been reviewed by Starr and Chatterjee (1972). *Erwinia carotovora* var. *carotovora*, *E. carotovora* var. *atroseptica* and *E. chrysanthemi* are a group of soft-rotting bacteria characterized by properties common to the Enterobacteriaceae, capable of producing acetoin and having strong pectolytic activity (Graham, 1964, 1971; Dye, 1969; Lelliott, 1974). *Erwinia chrysanthemi* can readily be distinguished from the other organisms in this group and to the author's knowledge isolation of this bacterium from potatoes has been reported only rarely (Graham, 1971; Tanii and Baba, 1971).

Strains of *E. carotovora* will grow in ammonium salts–glucose media (Starr and Mandel, 1950; Dye, 1969) but the growth rate is improved by addition of vitamins (Starr and Chatterjee, 1972). The organisms are facultative anaerobes and will grow in conditions of restricted aeration. In the presence of 3% CO_2 growth of var. *atroseptica* and of var. *carotovora* decreased with decreasing concentration of O_2 in the range 21% to 0%, but in the absence of CO_2 negligible growth occurred at all O_2 concentrations. A CO_2 concentration greater than 10% was necessary to cause significant inhibition of the bacteria (Wells, 1974). The minimum and maximum growth temperatures reported are: for var. *atroseptica* 3° and 32–35° (Burkolder and Smith, 1949), 1–2·8° and 36–38° (Elliott, 1951); for var. *carotovora* 6° and 35–37° (Burkholder and Smith, 1949) and 4° and 38–39° (Elliott, 1951).

Erwinia carotovora var. *atroseptica* and var. *carotovora* differ in their pathogenicity to potato plants; both will cause blackleg at temperatures of 24·5° and above, whereas only strains of var. *atroseptica* will do so at 19° and below (Graham and Dowson, 1960; Graham, 1964). The biochemical and physiological properties which are most generally useful for distinguishing between var. *atroseptica* and var. *carotovora* are: formation of reducing substances from sucrose; formation of acid from α-methylglucoside and from maltose; ability to grow at 37° or 36° (Dye, 1969; Lelliott, 1974). The reducing compounds formed by *E. carotovora* var. *atroseptica* growing in a sucrose medium are mainly palatinose and 1-0-α-D-glucosyl-fructose (Lund and Wyatt, 1973) but in the case of other species of *Erwinia* the reducing compounds formed are mainly mixtures of glucose and fructose (Lund, 1975).

Several workers have studied the serology of soft-rot *Erwinia* from the point of view of antigenic structure and relationship between the strains (Elrod, 1941; Okabe and Goto, 1956; Goto and Okabe, 1957, 1958a; Stapp, 1961; Liu, 1970; Lazar, 1971; Samson, 1973). The earlier work was reviewed by Graham (1964). These studies showed considerable heterogenicity of antigenic structure, particularly in strains of *E. carotovora* var. *carotovora*, and the presence of some common antigens in strains of var. *carotovora* and var. *atroseptica*. Nevertheless, serological methods have proved to be useful aids in the identification of *E. carotovora* in plant material and on isolation plates. Agglutination tests using antiserum against *E. carotovora* var. *atroseptica* isolated from potato have been used to detect this organism in potato stems and rotting tubers (Novakova, 1957; Graham, 1963, 1971). Cross reactions occurred with some strains of var. *carotovora* and also with one strain of *Klebsiella* sp. and two of *Pseudomonas fluorescens* out of a range of other bacteria tested (Graham, 1963) indicating the need for confirmation of results. Use of a double-diffusion test and adsorption of the var. *atroseptica* antiserum with serologically related strains of var. *carotovora* has been reported to offer a more reliable method for detecting *E. carotovora* var. *atroseptica* in potato stems and tubers (Vruggink and Maas Geesteranus, 1975). Provided a specific antiserum is available, a fluorescent-antibody stain can be a sensitive and rapid means of detecting *E. carotovora* var. *atroseptica* (Allen and Kelman, 1975).

Enzymes in relation to maceration of potato tissue

Pectic enzymes are considered to play a major role in maceration of plant tissue (Bateman and Millar, 1966). Strains of *E. carotovora* form extra-cellular and intracellular endopectate lyase, EC 4.2.2.2., (Starr and Moran, 1962; Moran *et al.*, 1968; Moran and Starr, 1969; Rombouts, 1972; Berndt, 1973), extracellular endopolygalacturonase, EC 3.2.1.15 (Nasuno and Starr, 1966; Rombouts, 1972; Berndt, 1973) and pectin-esterase, EC 3.1.1.11. (Nasuno and Starr, 1966; de Herrera, 1972; Rombouts, 1972). In addition exopectate lyase, EC 4.2.2.9, (Okamoto *et al.*, 1963, 1964a, 1964b, 1964c), exopolygalacturonase, EC 3.2.1.82 (Hatanaka and Ozawa, 1969, 1971) and oligogalacturonide lyase, EC 4.2.2.6, (Moran *et al.*, 1968b; Hatanaka and Ozawa, 1970) have been extracted from the bacterial cells.

Purified endopectate lyase of *E. carotovora* causes degradation of potato cell walls and loss of electrolytes, tissue maceration and death of potato tuber cells (Dean and Wood, 1967; Mount *et al.*, 1970; Tseng and Mount, 1974). In the case of purified endopectate lyases of *E. carotovora* and of *E. chrysanthemi*, damage to the membrane of potato cells is prob-ably a secondary effect resulting from loss of ability of the enzymically-degraded cell walls to support the cell membrane (Stephens and Wood, 1975; Basham and Bateman, 1975a, 1975b).

Cellulases do not appear generally to contribute significantly to the initial stages of maceration of plant tissue (Bateman and Millar, 1966). Several workers have reported the ability of strains of *E. carotovora* to degrade soluble forms of cellulose (Amman, 1952; Goto and Okabe, 1958b, 1959; Berndt, 1973; Beraha *et al.*, 1974) but 50 strains of *E. carotovora* var. *atroseptica* studied by Graham (1964) and 10 strains of var. *atroseptica* and 50 of var. *carotovora* studied by Dye (1969) failed to do so. In contrast, some strains of *E. chrysanthemi* show active cellulase (C_x) activity (Dye, 1969; Garibaldi and Bateman, 1970).

The relationship between virulence of *E. carotovora*, measured by ability to cause maceration of plant tissue, and enzyme production has been studied by Beraha *et al.* (1974). A virulent parent strain showed high activity of polygalacturonase, pectate lyase, cellulase (C_x) and phosphatidase. In the case of mutants induced by treatment with N-methyl-N^1-nitro-N-nitrosoguanidine and selected for avirulence activity of all four enzymes was reduced, and a virulent revertant strain derived from an avirulent mutant showed high activity of all these enzymes. Two virulent, phosphatidase-deficient mutants from the virulent parent strain had reduced pectate lyase and C_x activity but relatively high polygalacturonase, suggesting that this polygalacturonase may be the significant enzyme in soft-rotting. More recently, genetic evidence (Chatterjee and Starr, 1977) has indicated that in the case of *E. chrysanthemi* pectate lyase, rather than polygalacturonase, played an essential role in maceration of plant tissue.

Isolation and Properties of Pectolytic Species of *Clostridium*

When extensive soft-rotting occurs in potatoes localized tissue becomes anaerobic and enrichment of pectolytic clostridia occurs. A double-layered, pectate medium containing polymyxin to suppress *E. carotovora* has been used for counting and isolation of these bacteria from potato tissue (Lund, 1972) (Fig. 9). Three main groups of pectolytic clostridia have been isolated at 20 or 25°. (1) Isolates which form oval, central or sub-terminal spores, and which resemble *C. butyricum* in morphology, sugars fermented and fermentation products from glucose. (2) Unidentified isolates which form round, sub-terminal spores. (3) Isolates which form oval, central or sub-terminal spores and produce a pink pigment, usually cell bound. These pink-pigmented clostridia differ from pigmented clostridia previously described (Breed *et al.*, 1957; Smith and Hobbs, 1974) and studies have been made of their general properties (Lund *et al.*, 1977) and of their pectic enzymes (Lund and Brocklehurst, 1978).

The Interaction Between *Erwinia carotovora* and Potato Tissue

The critical effect of depletion of oxygen on initiation of rotting in potatoes was referred to earlier. Tubers inoculated with a suspension of *E. carotovora* and incubated with a constant supply of air are extremely resistant to soft-rot even when incubated at the optimum temperature and in a saturated atmosphere, whereas depletion of oxygen in the atmosphere leads to extensive decay (Leach, 1930; Murant and Wood, 1957a, 1957b;

FIG. 9. Colonies of a pectolytic *Clostridium* sp. on pectate medium (Lund, 1972) after incubation for 2 days at 25° under H_2 + 10% CO_2.

Lipton, 1967; Nielsen, 1968; Scholey, Marshall and Whitbread, 1968; Lund and Nicholls, 1970; Lund and Wyatt, 1972). By inoculating strains of *E. carotovora* var. *atroseptica* and var. *carotovora* onto discs of tuber tissue, Pérombelon (1971c) found ED_{50} values per tuber disc of 1 to 5·2 bacteria in anaerobic conditions and 8·7 to 508 in air. De Boer (1976) inoculated whole tubers with *E. carotovora* var. *atroseptica* and obtained ED_{50} values per injection site of approximately 10^5 bacteria in an atmosphere of 2% oxygen, 6·5 × 10^7 in 15% oxygen and by extrapolation calculated ED_{50} values of 10^4 bacteria in the absence of oxygen and 10^9 to 10^{10} bacteria in air.

The processes which are considered to contribute to resistance of tubers to *E. carotovora* are all oxygen dependent. These processes include (1) suberization and periderm formation under wounded tissue; (2) oxidation of phenols to antibacterial quinones; (3) formation of other antibacterial compounds in response to infection. In addition to inhibiting these reactions, absence of oxygen may also affect the integrity of cell membranes causing leakage of water and solutes from turgid potato cells and encouraging growth of bacteria (Pérombelon and Lowe, 1975).

If damaged potatoes are stored in suitable conditions wound-healing occurs. Suberin is deposited in a layer of cells under damaged tissue and subsequently suberized periderm is formed (Priestley and Woffenden, 1923; Artschwager, 1927). This process of wound-healing is inhibited in anaerobic conditions (Priestley and Woffenden, 1923; Leach, 1930, 1931); it is also delayed by treatment of tubers with sprout suppressants, such as propham and chlorpropham, that inhibit mitosis (Audia et al., 1962). The healed surfaces protect the tissue against organisms which can penetrate freshly exposed wounds (Leach, 1930; Rudd-Jones and Dowson, 1950; Smith and Smart, 1955). A complete band of suberized cells can form an effective barrier against E. carotovora var. atroseptica (Fox et al., 1971) but, depending on temperature and relative humidity, the bacterium has been reported to penetrate the suberized layer (Rudd-Jones and Dowson, 1950). The extent and type of damage and the presence of liquid at the damage site may influence the rate of wound-healing and hence the development of soft-rot. In tissue with an adequate supply of oxygen wound-healing may play a major part in preventing extensive bacterial soft-rot.

Mechanical damage to plant tissue and infection by micro-organisms frequently causes an increase in polyphenoloxidase activity (Kosuge, 1969; Pierpoint, 1970; Uritani, 1971). Potato halves containing a well inoculated with E. carotovora developed a zone of white, rotted tissue bounded by a ring of blackened tissue which acted as an infection barrier (Lovrekovitch et al., 1967). A similar zone of blackened tissue was formed when tuber halves were treated with a preparation containing pectic enzymes. It was suggested that this black infection barrier resulted from oxidation of phenolic compounds by polyphenoloxidase in tissue disrupted by the bacterial pectic enzymes. In the presence of glucose high concentrations of bacteria prevented the oxidation of catechol by a commercial polyphenoloxidase preparation; this effect was attributed to the activity of a cell-bound, bacterial dehydrogenase and could account for the failure of phenolic compounds to be oxidized in the white, rotted tissue.

When tubers inoculated with E. carotovora are incubated at 20° with a continuous supply of humidified air, a brown, restricted type of rot generally occurs and the terpenoid compounds rishitin, phytuberin and lubimin are formed in infected tissue but are not formed when inoculated tubers are deprived of oxygen (Lyon, 1972; Beczner and Lund, 1975; Beczner et al., 1975). These compounds had previously been reported as phytoalexins formed by potato tubers in response to infection with incompatible races of Phytophthora infestans (Tomiyama et al., 1968; Varns et al., 1971; Metlitskii et al., 1971; Kuc, 1972). The possibility was investigated that rishitin and phytuberin might have sufficient antibacterial activity to contribute to resistance of tubers to *E. carotovora*. Rishitin, but not phytuberin, at concentrations similar to those found in rotting tissue caused some inhibition of growth of *E. carotovora* and had a bactericidal effect in 0·1% peptone solution (Lyon and Bayliss, 1975). In maincrop tubers of several cultivars, no correlation was found between extent of rotting and concentration of rishitin and phytuberin formed (Lyon *et al.*, 1975). Neither rishitin nor phytuberin, at concentrations found in infected tissue, had any inhibitory effect on polygalacturonase or pectate lyase activity of *E. carotovora* var. *atroseptica* (B. M. Lund and C. E. Bayliss, unpublished). However, since rishitin, at concentrations similar to those found in infected tissue, has some inhibitory effect on *E. carotovora*, it may contribute to resistance of tubers to bacterial soft-rot.

Future Developments

If changes are proposed in methods for handling and storage of potatoes, e.g. the introduction of washing before storage (Orr *et al.*, 1976) tests of the soft-rot potential of tubers (Lund and Kelman, 1977) before and after treatment could be used to show whether the process is likely to result in an increased risk of soft-rot during storage. The role of individual factors affecting soft-rot potential can be analysed by subjecting tubers to controlled treatments, such as physical damage, immersion in water and inoculation with soft-rot bacteria, before incubation in a mist chamber. Assessments of the inherent resistance of potatoes, the effect of environmental factors and the virulence of soft-rot bacteria can be made most effectively by treating tubers with a range of inocula of bacteria and incubating in the required environment (De Boer *et al.*, 1975).

In view of the frequent occurrence of pectolytic clostridia in tubers affected by soft-rot in store or induced to rot in the laboratory, further assessments should be made of the possibility that these anaerobic bacteria are a significant cause of spoilage in practical conditions.

With regard to studies of the ecology and of the virulence of *E. carotovora* a further investigation should be made of the differentiation between var. *atroseptica* and var. *carotovora* according to pathogenicity in potato plants (Graham and Dowson, 1960). Such an investigation should include isolates of both organisms from temperate regions, and from other vegetables in addition to potatoes. Studies of the dissemination of these bacteria in crops are being continued in Scotland in relation to the production of seed-potatoes free from *E. carotovora*.

Acknowledgements

I am grateful to Dr. D. C. Graham, Department of Agriculture and Fisheries for Scotland, Agricultural Scientific Services, East Craigs, Edinburgh, and Dr. J. L. Peel and Professor S. R. Elsden, ARC Food Research Institute, Norwich, for constructive criticism of this paper.

References

ADAMS, M. J. (1975). Potato tuber lenticels: susceptibility to infection by *Erwinia carotovora* var. *atroseptica* and *Phytophthora infestans*. *Annals of Applied Biology*, **79**, 275–282.

ALLEN, E. & KELMAN, A. (1975). Detection of *Erwinia carotovora* var. *atroseptica* in mixed cultures, potato tubers, soil, insects and potato leaves by immuno-fluorescent staining procedures. *Proceedings of the American Phytopathology Society*, **2**, 68 (Abstr.).

AMMAN, A. (1952). Über die Bildung von Zellulase bei pathogenen Mikroorganismen. *Phytopathologische Zeitschrift*, **18**, 416–446.

ARTSCHWAGER, E. (1927). Wound periderm in the potato as affected by temperature and humidity. *Journal of Agricultural Research*, **35**, 995–1000.

AUDIA, W. V., SMITH, W. L., Jnr. & CRAFT, C. C. (1962). Effects of isopropyl N-(3-chlorophenyl) carbamate on suberin, periderm and decay development of Katahdin potato slices. *The Botanical Gazette*, **123**, 255–258.

BASHAM, H. G. & BATEMAN, D. F. (1975a). Killing of plant cells by pectic enzymes: the lack of direct injurious interaction between pectic enzymes or their soluble reaction products and plant cells. *Phytopathology*, **65**, 141–153.

BASHAM, H. G. & BATEMAN, D. F. (1975b). Relationship of cell death in plant tissue treated with a homogeneous endopectate lyase to cell wall degradation. *Physiological Plant Pathology*, **5**, 249–262.

BATEMAN, D. F. & MILLAR, R. L. (1966). Pectic enzymes in tissue degradation. *Annual Review of Phytopathology*, **4**, 119–146.

BECZNER, J. & LUND, B. M. (1975). The production of lubimin by potato tubers inoculated with *Erwinia carotovora* var. *atroseptica*. *Acta phytopathologica academiae scientiarum Hungaricae*, **10**, 269–274.

BECZNER, J., LUND, B. M. & BAYLISS, C. E. (1975). The occurrence of rishitin, phytuberin and spirovetiva-1 (10, 11-dien-2-one) in potato tubers inoculated with *Erwinia carotovora* var. *atroseptica* or with *Phytophthora infestans*. *Proceedings of the American Phytopathological Society*, **2**, 121 (Abstr.).

BERAHA, L., GARBER, E. D. & BILLETER, B. A. (1974). Enzyme profiles and virulence in mutants of *Erwinia carotovora*. *Phytopathologische Zeitschrift*, **81**, 15–23.

BERNDT, H. (1973). Investigations on the synthesis of some extracellular enzymes by *Erwinia carotovora*. *Archiv fur Mikrobiologie*, **91**, 137–148.

BÉTENCOURT, A. & PRUNIER, J. P. (1965). A propos de la pourriture seche lenticellaire des tubercules de pommes de terre provoquee par *Erwinia carotovora* (Jones) Holland. *European Potato Journal*, **8**, 230–242.

BONDE, R. (1950). Factors affecting potato blackleg and seed-piece decay. *The Maine Agricultural Experiment Station Bulletin*, **482**, 31pp.

BONDE, R. (1953). Preliminary studies of the control of bacterial decay of the potato with antibiotics. *American Potato Journal*, **30**, 143–147.

BOYD, A. E. W. (1972). Potato storage diseases. *Review of Plant Pathology*, **51**, 297–321.

BREED, R. S., MURRAY, E. G. D. & SMITH, N. R. (1957). *Bergey's manual of determinative bacteriology*. 7th edn. London: Ballière, Tindall and Cox.

BURKHOLDER, W. H. & SMITH, W. L. (1949). *Erwinia atroseptica* (van Hall) Jennison and *Erwinia carotovora* (Jones) Holland. *Phytopathology*, **39**, 887–897.

BURTON, W. G. (1950). Studies on the dormancy and sprouting of potatoes. 1. The oxygen content of the potato tuber. *New Phytologist*, **49**, 121–134.

BURTON, W. G. (1963). The basic principles of potato storage as practised in Great Britain. *European Potato Journal*, **6**, 77–92.

BURTON, W. G. (1966). *The potato*. 2nd edn. Wageningen: H. Veenman and Zonen.

BURTON, W. G. & WIGGINTON, M. J. (1970). The effect of a film of water upon the oxygen status of a potato. *Potato Research*, **13**, 180–186.

CHATTERJEE, A. K. & STARR, M. P. (1977). Donor strains of the soft-rot bacterium *Erwinia chrysanthemi* and conjugational transfer of the pectolytic capacity. *Journal of Bacteriology*, **132**, 862–869.

CHURCH, B. M., HAMPSON, C. P. & FOX, W. R. (1970). The quality of stored main crop potatoes in Great Britain. *Potato Research*, **13**, 41–58.

CROMARTY, R. W. & EASTON, G. D. (1973). The incidence of decay and factors affecting bacterial soft rot of potatoes. *American Potato Journal*, **50**, 398–407.

CUPPELS, D. & KELMAN, A. (1974). Evaluation of selective media for isolation of soft-rot bacteria from soil and plant tissue. *Phytopathology*, **64**, 468–475.

DEAN, M. & WOOD, R. K. S. (1967). Cell wall degradation by a pectate transeliminase. *Nature, London*, **214**, 408–410.

DE BOER, S. H. (1976). Ecology of *Erwinia carotovora* and factors affecting tuber susceptibility to bacterial soft rot. Ph.D. Thesis, University of Wisconsin-Madison.

DE BOER, S. H., CUPPELS, D. A. & KELMAN, A. (1974). Populations of pectolytic *Erwinia* spp. in the rhizosphere of potato plants. *Proceedings of the American Phytopathological Society*, **1**, 124 (Abstr.).

DE BOER, S. H., KELMAN, A. & BUELOW, F. H. (1975). An improved method for measuring influence of chemical treatments and environmental factors on susceptibility of potato tubers to *Erwinia* soft rot in storage. Proceedings of the American Phytopathological Society **2**, 68 (Abstr.).

DE HERRERA, E. C. (1972). Production of pectinmethylesterase by *Erwinia carotovora*. *Phytopathologische Zeitschrift*, **74**, 48–54.

DOWSON, W. J. (1943). Spore-forming bacteria in potatoes. *Nature, London*, **152**, 331.

DOWSON, W. J. (1944). Spore-forming bacteria pathogenic to plants. *Nature, London*, **154**, 557.

DOWSON, W. J. & RUDD-JONES, D. (1951). Bacterial wet rot of potato tubers following *Phytophthora infestans*. *Annals of Applied Biology*, **38**, 231–236.

DYE, D. W. (1969). A taxonomic study of the genus *Erwinia*. II. The *carotovora* group. *New Zealand Journal of Science*, **12**, 81–97.

ELLIOTT, C. (1951). *Manual of bacterial plant pathogens*. 2nd edn. Waltham, Mass: Chronica Botanica Co.

ELROD, R. P. (1941). Serological studies of the *Erwiniae*. II. Soft rot group with some serological considerations. *Botanical Gazette*, **103**, 266–279.

FERGUSON, T. P. (1969). Storage of Potatoes for the Processing Industry. *Food World*, **4**, 18–22.

FICKE, W., NAUMANN, K., SKADOW, K., MULLER,, H. J. & ZIELKE, R. (1973) Die. Lebensdauer von *Pectobacterium carotovorum* var. *atrosepticum* (Van Hall) Dowson auf dem Pflanzgut und im Boden. *Archiv für Phytopathologie und Pflanzenschutz.*, **9**, 281–293.

FOX, R. T. V., MANNERS, J. G. & MYERS, A. (1971). Ultrastructure of entry and spread of *Erwinia carotovora* var. *atroseptica* into potato tubers. *Potato Research*, **14**, 61–73.

FOX, R. T. V., MANNERS, J. G. & MYERS, A. (1972). Ultrastructure of tissue disintegration and host reactions in potato tubers infected by *Erwinia carotovora* var. *atroseptica*. *Potato Research*, **15**, 130–145.

GARIBALDI, A. & BATEMAN, D. F. (1970). Association of pectolytic and cellulolytic enzymes with bacterial slow wilt of Carnation caused by *Erwinia chrysanthemi* Burkh., McFad. et Dim. *Phytopathologia Mediterranea*, **9**, 136–144.

GOTO, M. & OKABE, N. (1957). Studies on the strains of *Erwinia carotovora* (Jones) Holland. IV. Antigenic variations. *Bulletin of the Faculty of Agriculture Schizuoka University*, **7**, 11–12.

GOTO, M. & OKABE, N. (1958a). Studies on the strains of *Erwinia carotovora* (Jones) Holland. V. Antigenic structures of soma, their relation to biochemical properties, and heat inactivation of agglutination. *Bulletin of the Faculty of Agriculture Schizuoka University*, **8**, 1–3.

GOTO, M. & OKABE, N. (1958b). Cellulolytic activity of phytopathogenic bacteria. *Nature, London*, **182**, 1516.

GOTO, M. & OKABE, N. (1959). Studies on the cellulolytic enzymes of phytopathogenic bacteria. Part 1. On the production of C_x-enzyme, Part 2, Relations between the activity of cellulase "C_x" and pH, reaction temperature or salts. *Annals of the Phytopathological Society of Japan*, **24**, 182–188.

GRAHAM, D. C. (1958). Occurrence of soft rot bacteria in Scottish soils. *Nature, London*, **61**, 61.

GRAHAM, D. C. (1962). Black Leg Disease of Potatoes. *Scottish Agriculture*, **41**, 211–215.

GRAHAM, D. C. (1963). Serological diagnosis of potato blackleg and tuber soft rot. *Plant Pathology*, **12**, 142–144.

GRAHAM, D. C. (1964). Taxonomy of the soft rot coliform bacteria. *Annual Review of Phytopathology*, **2**, 13–42.

GRAHAM, D. C. (1971). Identification of soft rot coliform bacteria. In *Proceedings of the Third International Conference on Plant Pathogenic Bacteria* (Maas Geesteranus, H. P., ed.) Wageningen: Centre for Agricultural Publishing and Documentation, 1972, pp. 273–279.

GRAHAM, D. C. & DOWSON, W. J. (1960). The coliform bacteria associated with potato blackleg and soft rots. I. Their pathogenicity in relation to temperature. *Annals of Applied Biology*, **48**, 51–57.

GRAHAM, D. C. & HARDIE, J. L. (1971). Prospects for control of potato blackleg disease by the use of stem cuttings. *Proceedings of the 6th British Insecticide and Fungicide Conference* 1971, pp. 219–225.

GRAHAM, D. C. & HARPER, P. C. (1967). Potato blackleg and tuber soft rot. *Scottish Agriculture*, **46**, 68.

GRAHAM, D. C. & HARRISON, M. D. (1975). Potential spread of *Erwinia* spp. in aerosols. *Phytopathology*, **65**, 739–741.

GRAHAM, D. C. & VOLCANI, Z. (1961). Experiments on the control of blackleg disease of potato by disinfection of seed tubers with mercury compounds and streptomycin. *European Potato Journal*, **4**, 129–137.

GRAHAM, D. C., QUINN, C. E. & HARRISON, M. D. (1976). Recurrence of soft rot coliform infections in potato stem cuttings: an epidemiological study on the central nuclear stock production farm in Scotland, 1967–74. *Potato Research*, **19**, 3–21.

HARPER, P. C., BOYD, A. E. W. & GRAHAM, D. C. (1963). Growth cracking and bacterial soft rot in potato tubers. *Plant Pathology*, **12**, 139–142.

HATANAKA, C. & OZAWA, J. (1969). Isolation of a new exopolygalacturonase producing digalacturonic acid from pectic acid. *Agricultural and Biological Chemistry*, **33**, 116–118.

HATANAKA, C. & OZAWA, J. (1970). An oligogalacturonate transeliminase from *Erwinia aroideae*. *Agricultural and Biological Chemistry*, **34**, 1618–1624.

HATANAKA, C. & OZAWA, J. (1971). Enzymic degradation of pectic acid. XIII. A new exopolygalacturonase producing digalacturonic acid from pectic acid. *Bericht des Ohara Instituts fur landwirtschaftliche Biologie*, **15**, 47–60.

HINGORANI, M. K. & ADDY, S. K. (1953). Factors influencing bacterial soft rot of potatoes. *Indian Phytopathology*, **6**, 110–115.

JACKSON, A. W. & HENRY, B. S. (1946). Occurrence of *Bacillus polymyxa* (Praz.) Mig. in Alberta soils with special reference to its pathogenicity in potato tubers. *Canadian Journal of Research Section C*, **24**, 39–46.

KENDRICK, J. B., WEDDING, R. T. & PAULUS, A. O. (1959). A temperature-relative humidity index for predicting the occurrence of bacterial soft rot of Irish potatoes. *Phytopathology*, **49**, 701–705.

KERR, A. (1953). A method of isolating soft rotting bacteria from soils. *Nature, London.*, **172**, 1155.

KIKUMOTO, T. (1974). Ecological studies on the soft rot bacteria of vegetables (13). The role of Chinese cabbage culture in the seasonal trends in the populations of the soft rot bacteria in soil. *Bulletin of the Institute for Agricultural Research, Tohoku University*, **25**, 125–137.

KIKUMOTO, T. & SAKAMOTO, M. (1967). Ecological studies on the soft rot bacteria of vegetables III. Application of immunofluorescent staining for the detection and counting of *Erwinia aroideae* in soil. *Annals of the Phytopathological Society of Japan*, **33**, 181–186.

KIKUMOTO, T. & SAKAMOTO, M. (1969a). Ecological studies on the soft rot bacteria of vegetables. VI. Influence of the development of various plants on the survival of *Erwinia aroideae* added to soil. *Annals of the Phytopathological Society of Japan*, **35**, 29–35.

KIKUMOTO, T. & SAKAMOTO, M. (1969b). Ecological studies on the soft rot bacteria of vegetables. VII. The preferential stimulation of the soft-rot bacteria in the rhizosphere of crop plants and weeds. *Annals of the Phytopathological Society of Japan*, **35**, 36–40.

KLINGNER, A. E., HILDEBRAND, D. C. & WILHELM, S. (1971). Occurrence of *Erwinia carotovora* in the rhizosphere of cotton plants which escape *Verticillium* wilt. *Plant and Soil*, **34**, 215–218.

KOSUGE, T. (1969). The role of phenolics in host response to infection. *Annual Review of Phytopathology*, **7**, 195–222.

KUC, J. (1972). Phytoalexins. *Annual Review of Phytopathology*, **10**, 207–232.

LAPWOOD, D. H. (1957). Studies on the physiology of parasitism. XXIII. On the parasitic vigour of certain bacteria in relation to their capacity to secrete pectolytic enzymes. *Annals of Botany, London N.S.*, **21**, 167–184.

LAPWOOD, D. H. & HIDE, G. A. (1971). Potato. In *Diseases of crop plants* (Western, J. H., ed.). London: Macmillan, pp. 89–122.

LAPWOOD, D. H. & LEGG, P. R. (1972). *Bacterial soft rots*. Rothamsted Experimental Station Report for 1972, Part 1, p. 147.

LAZAR, I. (1971). Serological relationships between the "*amylovora*", "*carotovora*" and "*herbicola*" groups of the genus *Erwinia*. In *Proceedings of the Third International Conference on Plant Pathogenic Bacteria* (Maas Geesteranus, H. P., ed.). Wageningen: Centre for Agricultural Publishing and Documentation, 1972, pp. 131–141.

LAZAR, I. & BUCUR, E. (1964). Recent research in Roumania on blackleg and bacterial soft-rot of potato. *European Potato Journal*, **7**, 102–108.

LEACH, J. G. (1930). Potato blackleg: the survival of the pathogen in the soil, and some factors influencing infection. *Phytopathology*, **20**, 734–751.

LEACH, J. G. (1931). Blackleg disease of potatoes in Minnesota. *University of Minnesota Agricultural Experiment Station Bulletin*, **76**, 33 pp.

LELLIOTT, R. A. (1974). Erwinia. In *Bergey's manual of determinative bacteriology*. 8th edn. (Buchanan, R. E. & Gibbons, N. E., eds). Baltimore: Williams and Wilkins, pp. 332–338.

LIPTON, W. (1967). Some effects of low-oxygen atmospheres on potato tubers. *American Potato Journal*, **44**, 292–299.

LIU, S. C. Y., (1970). Antigenic and immunodiffusional analysis of *Erwinia carotovora* and *Erwinia atroseptica*. *Phytopathology*, **60**, 1300–1301 (Abstr.).

LOGAN, C. (1963). A selective medium for the isolation of soft rot coliforms from soil. *Nature, London*, **199**, 623.

LOGAN, C. (1964). Bacterial hard rot of potato. *European Potato Journal*, **7**, 45–56.

LOGAN, C. (1968). The survival of the potato blackleg pathogen overwinter. *Record of Agricultural Research, Ministry of Agriculture of Northern Ireland*, **17**, 115–121.

LOVREKOVITCH, L., LOVREKOVITCH, H. & STAHMANN, M. A. (1967). Inhibition of phenol oxidation by *Erwinia carotovora* in potato tissue and its significance in disease resistance. *Phytopathology*, **57**, 737–742.

LUND, B. M. (1971). Bacterial spoilage of vegetables and certain fruits. *Journal of Applied Bacteriology*, **34**, 9–20.

LUND, B. M. (1972). Isolation of pectolytic clostridia from potatoes. *Journal of Applied Bacteriology*, **35**, 609–614.

LUND, B. M. (1975). Formation of reducing sugars from sucrose by *Erwinia* species. *Journal of General Microbiology*, **88**, 367–371.

LUND, B. M. & BROCKLEHURST, T. F. (1978). Pectic enzymes of pigmented strains of *Clostridium*. *Journal of General Microbiology*, **104**, 59–66.

LUND, B. M. & KELMAN, A. (1977). Determination of the potential for development of bacterial soft rot of potatoes. *American Potato Journal*, **54**, 211–225.

LUND, B. M. & NICHOLLS, J. C. (1970). Factors influencing the soft-rotting of potatoes by bacteria. *Potato Research*, **13**, 210–214.

LUND, B. M. & WYATT, G. M. (1972). The effect of oxygen and carbon dioxide concentrations on bacterial soft rot of potatoes. I. King Edward potatoes inoculated with *Erwinia carotovora* var. *atroseptica*. *Potato Research*, **15**, 174–179.

LUND, B. M. & WYATT, G. M. (1973). The nature of reducing compounds formed from sucrose by *Erwinia carotovora* var. *atroseptica*. *Journal of General Microbiology*, **78**, 331–336.

LUND, B. M., BROCKLEHURST, T. F. & WYATT, G. M. (1979). In preparation.

LYON, G. D. (1972). Occurrence of rishitin and phytuberin in potato tubers inoculated with *Erwinia carotovora* var. *atroseptica*. *Physiological Plant Pathology*, **2**, 411–416.

LYON, G. D. & BAYLISS, C. E. (1975). The effect of rishitin on *Erwinia carotovora* var. *atroseptica* and other bacteria. *Physiological Plant Pathology*, **6**, 177–186.

LYON, G. D., LUND, B. M., BAYLISS, C. E. & WYATT, G. M. (1975). Resistance of potato tubers to *Erwinia carotovora* and formation of rishitin and phytuberin in infected tissue. *Physiological Plant Pathology*, **6**, 43–50.

MAFF (1972). *Potatoes*. Bulletin 94. 5th edn. London: HMSO.

MALCOLMSON, J. F. (1959). A study of *Erwinia* isolates obtained from soft rots and blackleg of potatoes. *Transactions of the British Mycological Society*, **42**, 261–269.

MAZZUCCHI, U. & DALLI, A. (1974). Bacterial soft rot of fennel (*Foeniculum vulgare* var. *dulce* Mill). *Phytopathologia Mediterranea*, **13**, 113–116.

MENELEY, J. C. & STANGHELLINI, M. E. (1976). Isolation of soft rot *Erwinia* spp. from agricultural soils using an enrichment technique. *Phytopathology*, **66**, 367–370.

METLITSKII, L. B., OZERETSKOVSKAYA, O. L., VULFSON, N. S. & CHALOVA, L. I. (1971). Effects of lubimin on potato resistance to *Phytophthora infestans* and its chemical identification. *Mikrobiologia i Fitopatologia*, **5**, 438–443.

MEW, T. W., HO, W. C. & CHU, L. (1976). Infectivity and survival of soft rot bacteria in Chinese cabbage. *Phytopathology*, **66**, 1325–1327.

MORAN, F. & STARR, M. P. (1969). Metabolic regulation of polygalacturonic acid trans-eliminase in *Erwinia*. *European Journal of Biochemistry*, **11**, 291–295.

MORAN, F., NASUNO, S. & STARR, M. P. (1968a). Extracellular and intracellular polygalacturonic acid trans-eliminases of *Erwinia carotovora*. *Archives of Biochemistry and Biophysics*, **123**, 298–306.

MORAN, F., NASUNO, S. & STARR, M. P. (1968b). Oligogalacturonide trans-eliminase of *Erwinia carotovora*. *Archives of Biochemistry and Biophysics*, **125**, 734–741.

MOUNT, M. S., BATEMAN, D. F. & BASHAM, H. G. (1970). Induction of electrolyte loss, tissue maceration and cellular death of potato tissue by an endopolygalacturonate trans-eliminase. *Phytopathology*, **60**, 924–931.

MURANT, A. F. & WOOD, R. K. S. (1957a). Factors affecting the pathogenicity of certain bacteria to potato tubers. I. *Annals of Applied Biology*, **45**, 635–649.

MURANT, A. F. & WOOD, R. K. S. (1957b). Factors affecting the pathogenicity of bacteria to potato tubers. II. *Annals of Applied Biology*, **45**, 650–663.

NASUNO, S. & STARR, M. P. (1966). Polygalacturonase of *Erwinia carotovora*. *Journal of Biological Chemistry*, **241**, 5298.

NAUMANN, K., ZIELKE, R., PETT, B., STACKEWICZ, H., & JANKE, C. (1976). Conditions for triggering off potato soft rot disease by latent infection of tubers. *Archiv. für Phytopathologie und Pflanzenschutz*, **12**, 87–99.

NIELSEN, L. W. (1968). Accumulation of respiratory CO_2 around potato tubers in relation to bacterial soft rot. *American Potato Journal*, **45**, 174–181.

NOVAKOVA, J. (1957). A new method for isolation of blackleg pathogens from diseased plants. *Phytopathologische Zeitschrift*, **29**, 72–74.

OKABE, N. & GOTO, M. (1956). Studies on the strains of *Erwinia carotovora*

(Jones) Holland, I. Antigenic structures of the flagella and their relations to pathogenicity and maltose fermentation. *Bulletin of the Faculty of Agriculture, Shizuoka University*, **6**, 16–32.

OKAMOTO, K., HATANAKA, C. & OZAWA, J. (1963). On the saccharifying pectolytic enzymes of *Erwinia aroidea*. *Agricultural and Biological Chemistry*, **27**, 596–7.

OKAMOTO, K., HATANAKA, C. & OZAWA, J. (1964a). A saccharifying pectate trans-eliminase of *Erwinia aroideae*. *Agricultural and Biological Chemistry*, **28**, 331–336.

OKAMOTO, K., HATANAKA, C. & OZAWA, J. (1964b). Some properties of the saccharifying pectate trans-eliminase of *Erwinia aroideae*. *Bericht des Ōhara Institutes für landwirtschaftliche Biologie*, **12**, 107–114.

OKAMOTO, K., HATANAKA, C. & OZAWA, J. (1964c). The mechanism of action of the saccharifying pectate trans-eliminase. *Bericht des Ōhara Institutes für landwirtschaftliche Biologie*, **12**, 115–119.

O'NEILL, R. & LOGAN, C. (1975). A comparison of various selective isolation media for their efficiency in the diagnosis and enumeration of soft rot coliform bacteria. *Journal of Applied Bacteriology*, **39**, 139–146.

ORR, P. H., YAEGER, E. C., HUEGELET, J. E. & NELSON, D. C. (1976). Preliminary results of washing and disinfecting potatoes prior to storage. *American Potato Journal*, **53**, 367 (Abstr.).

PÉROMBELON, M. C. M. (1968). Bacterial soft rot and blackleg of potato. *Report of the Scottish Horticultural Research Institute* 1967, 33–34.

PÉROMBELON, M. C. M. (1971a). A quantal method for determining numbers of *Erwinia carotovora* var. *carotovora* and *E. carotovora* var. *atroseptica* in soils and plant material. *Journal of Applied Bacteriology*, **34**, 793–799.

PÉROMBELON, M. C. M. (1971b). A semi selective medium for estimating population densities of pectolytic *Erwinia* spp. in soil and in plant material. *Potato Research*, **14**, 158–160.

PÉROMBELON, M. C. M. (1971c). A quantitative method for assessing virulence of *Erwinia carotovora* var. *carotovora* and *E. carotovora* var. *atroseptica* and susceptibility to rotting of potato tissue. In *Proceedings of the Third International Conference on Plant Pathogenic Bacteria* (Maas Geesteranus, H. P., ed). Wageningen: Centre for Agricultural Publishing and Documentation, 1972, pp. 299–305.

PÉROMBELON, M. C. M. (1972). The extent and survival of contamination of potato stocks in Scotland by *Erwinia carotovora* var. *carotovora* and *E. carotovora* var. *atroseptica*. *Annals of Applied Biology*, **71**, 111–117.

PÉROMBELON, M. C. M. (1973). Sites of contamination and numbers of *Erwinia carotovora* present in stored seed potato stocks in Scotland. *Annals of Applied Biology*, **74**, 59–65.

PÉROMBELON, M. C. M. (1974). The role of the seed tuber in the contamination by *Erwinia carotovora* of potato crops in Scotland. *Potato Research*, **17**, 187–199.

PÉROMBELON, M. C. M. (1975). Observations on the survival of potato groundkeepers in Scotland. *Potato Research*, **18**, 205–215.

PÉROMBELON, M. C. M. (1976) Effects of environmental factors during the growing season on the level of potato tuber contamination by *Erwinia carotovora*. *Phytopathologische Zeitschrift*, **85**, 97–116.

PÉROMBELON, M. C. M. & LOWE, R. (1971). Bacterial soft rot and blackleg of potato. *Report of the Scottish Horticultural Research Institute* 1970, pp. 32–33.

PÉROMBELON, M. C. M. & LOWE, R. (1975). Studies on the initiation of bacterial soft rot in potato tubers. *Potato Research*, **18**, 64–82.

PÉROMBELON, M. C. M., LOWE, R. & BALLANTINE, E. M. (1976). Contamination by *Erwinia carotovora* of seed potato stocks of stem cutting origin in the process of multiplication. *Potato Research*, **19**, 335–349.

PÉROMBELON, M. C. M., GULLINGS-HANDLE, J. & KELMAN, A. (1977). In preparation.

PIERPOINT, W. S. (1970). Formation and behaviour of o-quinones in some processes of agricultural importance. *Rothamsted Experimental Station*. Report for 1970, Part 2, pp. 199–218.

POTATO MARKETING BOARD (UK) (1974). *National Damage Survey*, 1973.

POTATO MARKETING BOARD (UK) (1975). *Sutton Bridge Experimental Station, Annual Review*.

PRIESTLEY, J. H. & WOFFENDEN, L. M. (1923). The healing of wounds in potato tubers and their propagation by cut sets. *Annals of Applied Biology*, **10**, 96–115.

RAMSEY, G. B. (1919). Studies on the viability of the potato blackleg organism. *Phytopathology*, **9**, 285–288.

RAMSEY, G. B., LUTZ., J. M., WERNER, H. O. & EDGARD, A. D. (1944). Experiments on shipping washed early potatoes. *Nebraska Agricultural Experiment Station Bulletin*, **364**, 32pp.

ROMBOUTS, F. M. (1972). *Occurrence and properties of bacterial pectate lyases*. Doctoral thesis. Wageningen. Agricultural Research Report 779. Centre for Agricultural Publishing and Documentation, Wageningen.

RUDD-JONES, D. & DOWSON, W. J. (1950). On the bacteria responsible for soft rot in stored potatoes, and the reaction of the tuber to invasion by *Bacterium carotovorum* (Jones) Lehmann and Neumann. *Annals of Applied Biology*, **37**, 563–569.

RUEHLE, G. D. (1940). Bacterial soft rot of potatoes in Southern Florida. *Florida Agricultural Experiment Station Bulletin*, **348**, 36pp.

SAMSON, R. (1973). Les *Erwinia* pectinolytiques. II. Recherches sur les antigenes somatiques d'*Erwinia carotovora* var. *chrysanthemi* (Burkholder) Dye 1969. *Annales de Phytopathologie*, **5**, 377–388.

SAMPSON, P. J. & HAYWARD, A. C. (1971). Some characteristics of pectolytic bacteria associated with potato in Tasmania. *Australian Journal of Biological Sciences*, **24**, 917–923.

SCHOLEY, J., MARSHALL, C. & WHITBREAD, R. (1968). A pathological problem associated with the pre-packaging of potato tubers. *Plant Pathology*, **17**, 135–139.

SHEKHAWAT, G. S., NAGAICH, B. B., RAJPAL, & KISHORE, V. (1976). Bacterial top rot: a new disease of the potato. *Potato Research*, **19**, 241–247.

SMITH, L. D. S. & HOBBS, G. (1974). Clostridium. In *Bergey's manual of determinative bacteriology*, 8th edn. (Buchanan, R. E. & Gibbons, N. E. eds). Baltimore: Williams and Wilkins, pp. 551–572.

SMITH, M. A. & RAMSEY, G. B. (1947). Bacterial lenticel infections of early potatoes. *Phytopathology*, **37**, 225–242.

SMITH, W. L. (1950). Pathogenic differences manifested by *Erwinia carotovora*. *Phytopathology*, **40**, 1011–1017.

SMITH, W. L. & SMART, H. F. (1955). Relation of soft rot development to protective barriers in Irish potato slices. *Phytopathology*, **45**, 649–654.

SMITTLE, D. A., THORNTON, R. E., PETERSON, C. L. & DEAN, B. B. (1974). Harvesting potatoes with minimum damage. *American Potato Journal*, **51**, 152–164.

STANGHELLINI, M. E. & MENELEY, J. C. (1975). Identification of soft-rot *Erwinia* associated with blackleg of potato in Arizona. *Phytopathology*, **65**, 86–87.

STAPP, C. 1961. *Bacterial plant pathogens*. Oxford: Oxford University Press, pp. 148–151.

STARR, M. P. & CHATTERJEE, A. K. (1972). The genus *Erwinia*: Enterobacteria pathogenic to plants and animals. *Annual Review of Microbiology*, **26**, 389–426.

STARR, M. P. & MANDEL, M. (1950). The nutrition of phytopathogenic bacteria IV. Minimal nutritive requirements of the genus *Erwinia*. *Journal of Bacteriology*, **60**, 669–672.

STARR, M. P. & MORAN, F. (1962). Eliminative split of pectic substances by phytopathogenic soft-rot bacteria. *Science*, **135**, 920–921.

STEPHENS, G. J. & WOOD, R. K. S. (1975). Killing of protoplasts by soft rot bacteria. *Physiological Plant Pathology*. **5**, 165–181.

STEWART, D. J. (1962). A selective-diagnostic medium for the isolation of pectinolytic organisms in the Enterobacteriaceae. *Nature, London*, **195**, 1023.

TANII, A. & AKAI, J. (1975). Blackleg of potato plant caused by a serologically specific strain of *E. carotovora* var. *carotovora*. *Annals of the Phytopathological Society of Japan*, **41**, 573–577.

TANII, A. & BABA, T. (1971). Bacterial plant diseases in Hokkaido. II. Bacterial stem rot of potato plant caused by *Erwinia chrysanthemi* Burkholder et al. (*Pectobacterium carotovorum* var. *chrysanthemi*). *The Bulletin of the Hokkaido Prefectural Agricultural Experiment Station*, **24**, 1–10.

THOMPSON, B. D. (1969). Chemicals for control of post-harvest decay of vegetables. In Symposium on vegetable storage. *Acta horticulturae*, **20**, 156–161.

TOGASHI, J. (1972). Studies on the outbreak of the soft-rot disease of Chinese Cabbage by *Erwinia aroideae* (Towns) Holland. *Report of the Institute for Agricultural Research of Tohoku University*, **23**, 17–52.

TOMIYAMA, K., SAKUMA, T., ISHIZAKA, N., SATO, N., KATSUI, N., TAGASUKI, M. & MASAMUNE, T. (1968). A new antifungal substance isolated from resistant potato tuber tissue infected by pathogens. *Phytopathology*, **58**, 115–116.

TSENG, T. C. & MOUNT, M. S. (1974). Toxicity of endopolygalacturonate transeliminase, phosphatidase and protease to potato and cucumber tissue. *Phytopathology*, **64**, 229–236.

TWISS, P. T. G. & JONES, M. P. (1965). A survey of wastage in bulk-stored maincrop potatoes in Great Britain. *European Potato Journal*, **8**, 154.

URITANI, I. (1971). Protein changes in diseased plants. *Annual Review of Phytopathology*, **9**, 211-234.

VAN DEN BOOM, T. (1967). Untersuchungen über die Voraussetzungen für das Austreten der Schwartzbeinigkeit der Kartoffel. *Phytopathologische Zeitschrift*, **58**, 239–276.

VARNS, J. L., KUC, J. & WILLIAMS, E. B. (1971). Terpenoid accumulation as a biochemical response of the potato tuber to *Phytophthora infestans*. *Phytopathology*, **61**, 174–177.

VORONKEVICH, I. V. (1960). On the survival in the soil of bacteria of the genus *Erwinia*—causal agents of soft rot in plants. *Bulletin de la Societe des naturalistes de Moscou Ser. Biol.*, **65**, 95. Abstract in *Review of Applied Mycology* **40**, 202 (1961).

VORONKEVICH, I. V. & BUTSEVICH, L. A. (1964). Importance of soil infection and conditions of potato growth for the development of "black leg". *Doklady*

BACTERIAL SOFT-ROT 49

Vsesoyuznoi akademii sel'sko-kho-zyaistvennykh nauk **9**, 30–33. Cited in *Review of Plant Pathology*, **45**, 1488, (1966).

VORONKEVITCH, I. V., MATVEEVA, E. V. & ODINTSOVA, M. A. (1972). The rhizosphere as the habitat of phytopathogenic bacteria. II. Significance of the rhizosphere in the life cycle of causal agents of soft rots. *Biologicheskie Nauki* **15**, 103–109. Cited in *Review of Plant Pathology*, **52**, 897 (1973).

VRUGGINK, H. & MAAS GEESTERANUS, H. P. (1975). Serological recognition of *Erwinia carotovora* var. *atroseptica* the causal organism of potato blackleg. *Potato Research*, **18**, 546–555.

WELLS, J. M. (1974). Growth of *Erwinia carotovora*, *E. atroseptica* and *Pseudomonas fluorescens* in low oxygen and high carbon dioxide atmospheres. *Phytopathology*, **64**, 1012–1015.

WIGGINTON, M. J. (1973). Diffusion of oxygen through lenticels in potato tuber. *Potato Research*, **16**, 85–86.

WILSON, J. B. & JOHNSTON, E. F. (1967). Reducing the incidence of bacterial lenticel infection in Fall-washed Maine potatoes. *American Potato Journal*, **44**, 342 (Abstr.).

ZIELKE, R., MULLER, H. J., FICKE, W., NAUMANN, K. & SKADOW, K. (1974). Beziehungen zwischen dem Befallsverlauf der Schwarzbeinigkeit im Kartoffelbestand under der Knollennassfäule im Erntegut. *Archiv fur Phytopathologie und Pflanzenschutz*, **10**, 255–262.

Fireblight: The Development of a Predictive System

EVE BILLING

East Malling Research Station, Maidstone, Kent, England

Fireblight is a bacterial disease of pear and apple and other members of the sub-tribe Pomoideae in the family Rosaceae (e.g. Hawthorn, Coton-. easter, Mountain Ash, Whitebeam, Pyracantha). It has long been wide-spread in North America and is also present in New Zealand, southern England and parts of north continental Europe where it was first reported in 1919, 1957 and 1966 respectively.

Infection occurs most readily through blossoms but young shoots are also commonly infected during storms, when there is wind or hail damage accompanied by rain. This exposes the vulnerable tissue of the leaf veins allowing infection, as in blossom, by low doses of the pathogen (Brooks, 1926; Crosse *et al.*, 1972).

The disease is most active in rapidly growing tissue and from blossom and shoot infections the disease spreads down to older twigs and branches where cankers form as the extension of infection ceases. This work is concerned as much with such infections and their reactivation as it is with blossom and shoot infections. Growth of most host plants is greatest from May to July and is usually favoured by high temperatures in conjunction with high soil moisture.

The most vulnerable period for infection is blossom time. The range of blossom times of susceptible hosts extends from April to July (Table 1). Some hosts, including pears may produce further blossom during the summer, or autumn or both and thus remain vulnerable during the warmer part of the growing season. In England, temperatures are low during their main bloom period so pears usually escape primary blossom infection but they can suffer severely in years when summer blossom is common.

Infected tools, insects, birds, wind and movement of infected plants or fruit have been implicated in the spread of infection, but rain splash and wind-blown rain are undoubtedly important in its local spread within and between trees as they are with other bacterial plant diseases where the presence of free water can greatly aid the infection process.

TABLE 1. Approximate range of blossom periods of fireblight hosts

Host	Range of blossom period[a]
Pear	Early April to mid May
Apple	Mid April to late May
Hawthorn	Early May to early June
Mountain ash	May
Whitebeam	Mid May to early June
Pyracantha	Mid May to late June
Cotoneaster	June to July

[a] Actual dates and duration may vary widely from season to season and the overlap is not as great as appears here.

The pathogen, *Erwinia amylovora*, is a member of the family Enterobacteriaceae. It grows well on a variety of bacteriological media at temperatures up to 30° so studies *in vitro* present no problem; their interpretation in relation to activity *in vivo* however must be approached with caution.

As with other bacteria, the main environmental factors limiting aerobic growth in a nutritionally adequate medium (at or near pH 7) are temperature and water activity (a_w). As these two factors are also of major importance in plant growth, it seemed that any system developed for prediction of the rate of multiplication of the pathogen in the host plant should take adequate account of both.

Published information provided an inadequate basis for assessing the effect of temperature on the growth rates of *E. amylovora* so the first step was to study this (Billing, 1974). Water relationships presented a more formidable problem because insufficient was known about the a_w at the sites of multiplication of the bacteria under different conditions, and it could not be readily measured *in vitro* and subsequently applied to the field situation. This variable was therefore approached indirectly from field experience (Billing, 1976).

The system described here depends primarily on daily temperature and rainfall values and a knowledge of blossom periods of the hosts in question. Its development and possible value for predicting the length of incubation periods (i.e. the time between infection and the production of a new supply of inoculum) is outlined and discussed here in relation to fireblight, a bacterial plant disease. The principles, however, may be applicable to other areas in biology where temperature and moisture are the main variables governing rate of growth.

Methods

The effect of temperature on the doubling time of Erwinia amylovora

Growth rates *in vitro* were determined using 50 ml yeast peptone broth (pH 6·8–7·0) in 250 ml Erlenmeyer flasks in a shaking water bath (Billing, 1974). Approximate values for growth rates *in vivo* were available for some temperatures (15, 18, 23 and 25°) from experiments with apple rootstocks (Eden-Green, 1972).

Potential doublings (PD) day^{-1} (Billing, 1976)

Thermographs for 15 growing seasons at East Malling were examined to determine the number of hours each day at different temperatures from 9–24° at 3°; temperature intervals below 9° were discounted and temperatures above 24° were scored as 24° (see growth rate results). The PD day^{-1} was estimated from the growth rate data *in vitro*. Maximum and minimum temperatures for each day over the same period were examined and the mean PD day^{-1} for each combination of maximum and minimum temperature was used to construct Table 2.

TABLE 2. Potential doublings (PD) day^{-1} from daily maximum and minimum temperatures

	Temperature°			Temperature°	
Max.	Min.	PD day^{-1}	Max.	Min.	PD day^{-1}
9–11	<9	0·0	21–23	<9	7·0
9–11	9–11	0·5	21–23	9–11	8·0
12–14	<9	0·5	21–23	12–14	9·0
12–14	9–11	1·0	21–23	15–17	10·5
12–14	12–14	1·5	21–23	18–20	12·0
15–17	<9	1·5	24	<9	9·0
15–17	9–11	2·0	24	9–11	10·0
15–17	12–14	2·5	24	12–14	11·0
15–17	15–17	4·5	24	15–17	12·0
18–20	<9	3·5	24	18–20	13·0[a]
18–20	9–11	4·5			
18–20	12–14	5·0			
18–20	15–17	7·0			
18–20	18–20	10·5			

[a] For maximum temperatures above 24° no change in score. In climates where minimum temperatures exceed 18°, additional values may be necessary but where maximum temperatures exceed 30° inhibition of growth might have to be allowed for.
Modified from Billing (1976).

Moisture index and incubation periods

The moisture index was ultimately obtained from daily rainfall data (R). Field records showed that the time between infection and the appearance of symptoms (the incubation period, I) was not dependent on temperature alone. In two well documented cases, the duration of the incubation period was similar though warm dry weather followed infection in one case and cool wet weather in the other. It was found that if daily rainfall (R) was scored on the basis of a half point for a trace up to 2·5 mm and one point for 2·5 mm or more, the similarity of the incubation periods (I) was explicable. Using 13 additional cases, there was a linear relationship between PD and I/R and the coefficient of correlation between PD and I/R was 0·85 ($p<0·001$) (Billing, 1976). An equation derived from regression lines is now used to determine the likely length of an incubation period (I) using accumulated values of PD and R starting on the day of infection. On this basis the incubation period should end when

$$I \leq \frac{\Sigma R (\Sigma PD + 6)}{36}.$$

Table 3 shows a worked example.

TABLE 3. Estimation of the duration of the incubation period (I)—worked example

Date	I	R	ΣR	PD	ΣPD	$\dfrac{\Sigma R(\Sigma PD + 6)}{36}$
July 7	0	1	1	8·0	8·0	$-^a$
8	1	0	1	12·0	20·0	$-^a$
9	2	0	1	13·0	33·0	1·1
10	3	0·5	1·5	12·0	45·0	2·1
11	4	1	2·5	9·0	54·0	4·2^b

^{a} Minimum ΣPD for completion = 30.
^{b} $I < \dfrac{\Sigma R(\Sigma PD + 6)}{36} \therefore I = 4.$

Infection days

It was known from both field and experimental work in England that, in the presence of free water, new infections could be initiated at temperatures below 18°. For the present it is assumed that on days during the growing season with 2·5 mm or more of rain (i.e. those where lack of moisture is not limiting growth) new infections are likely to be initiated or old ones reactivated regardless of temperature. This definition may need to be extended, at least during blossom periods (see below), to include days with less rain, especially when maximum temperatures exceed 18° (Mills, 1955; Luepschen *et al.*, 1961).

Weather stations

Ideally, temperature and rainfall records should be taken at all orchards or nurseries where predictions are required. In practice, this is not feasible. A compromise solution is to take records from several stations in the main areas concerned and to report general trends in potential fireblight activity.

Field records

Records of the number of infected trees reported are available for the years 1958–1968. Personal field records were used for 1968 and subsequent years.

Results

The main findings are summarized only briefly here; a detailed account will be published elsewhere (in preparation). Weather data for the growing seasons 1958–1976 were analysed using records from two Kent weather stations and, over some years, from additional areas in southeast England. The results were presented in graphical form as in Fig. 1 so that the concentration and linking of incubation periods could be seen and related to blossom periods and field records for the season concerned. Only rarely were field data available close to a weather station but the varying trends in weather patterns in different seasons seemed to be related to the overall incidence of fireblight and to explain patterns of infection in different hosts in different seasons. The correlation between the number of infected trees reported in Kent (1958–1968) and the number of days in the growing season with 2·5 mm or more rain was 0·821 ($p < 0·01$) and that between the number of infected trees and the number of completed incubation periods in the growing season was 0·907 ($p < 0·001$). In both cases, the year 1963 was omitted because there was good reason to believe that the number of infected trees reported that year greatly underestimated the true situation (Billing, in preparation).

Further tests of the system involved checking available field records for each season against the weather graphs. Spring blossom infections have been rare in England so few were available for test and, whilst the system appeared to reflect trends in fireblight infections during most of the season, it seemed to overestimate the length of the incubation periods when infection occurred in April or early May. It seemed possible, from work in USA on epidemic apple blossom blight (Mills, 1955; Luepschen *et al.*, 1961; Powell, 1965), that at that time of year, moisture was not a limiting factor and that multiplication rates of the pathogen were largely temperature dependent. That this was a reasonable assumption is supported by the work of Goode (1975) who noted that the water demands of apple trees were low until the latter half of May: after that time, the mean daily evapotranspiration rate is about $2 \cdot 5$ mm day^{-1}, i.e. the value obtained here when moisture was no longer a limiting factor.

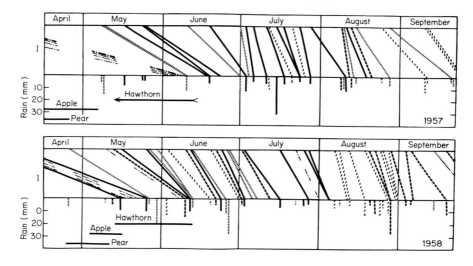

FIG. 1. Plot of estimated incubation periods (I) 1957 and 1958 (East Malling). Black and hatched lines are used to distinguish I lines that run parallel. Successive incubation periods (where rain fell within one day of the end of each I line) are shown in the same style. Note close succession in July 1957 at a time when summer blossom is common and was profuse that year; fireblight was first noticed in pear orchards that month. Horizontal lines show approximate blossom periods (the arrow in 1957 indicates that records were lacking but hawthorn blossom was likely to have been earlier than usual that year). Note apparent favourability of weather for fireblight at hawthorn blossom time in 1958 compared with 1957; the first recorded case on hawthorn was for that season (reported early 1959).

Calculated soil moisture deficits also are usually low in early May. It is possible that the same holds true at the end of the growing season (late September and October) when water demands again fall off. Few field observations were available to thoroughly test this possibility in England, but it was found with those available that, if R was scored as 1·0 for every day up to 15 May and in the standard way thereafter, a better fit was obtained. In other climates where trees bloom later, this modified scoring might have to continue for a longer or shorter period. This area needs further exploration in relation to flowering and the increase in water demand for transpiration as leaves expand and mature; with ornamental hosts, leaves commonly appear before blossom or the plants may be evergreen.

Prediction

The system is used predictively by daily checks on the start and completion of incubation periods. Where three or more incubation periods follow one another in quick succession, there is risk of epidemic blight or rapid downward spread of earlier infections with a potential for copious inoculum production and release, if inoculum was present at the start. If there is a damaging storm in summer at the end of an incubation period where there has been earlier build-up of infection, shoot blight is likely.

The system can only suggest trends and, like any forecasting system, is concerned with possibilities and probabilities, not with certainties, especially where the weather station is far from the infected area concerned. It must take into account blossom periods and shoot damage and additional factors which may affect the time of appearance of symptoms e.g. the likely dose of inoculum and the state of growth of the infected tissue. With fireblight, there is no way of assessing inoculum potential except by observation of existing infections. This system, however, should give an indication of periods of low and high risk so that time and money spent on seeking and destroying sources of infection can be used to best advantage.

In other climates, the system may have to be modified to allow for differences in temperature and rates of evapotranspiration and the times of bloom, but the principles should still hold true, i.e. that there is an interaction between moisture and temperature and that during the main part of the growing season, moisture is an important limiting factor for multiplication of the fireblight pathogen. How far irrigation can be equated with rain in this context is not known.

This system as it stands needs to be thoroughly tested to see if and where modification may be necessary for particular conditions. Where modifications are attempted, the underlying principles of the system must always be borne in mind; rainfall is far more likely to be the variable which is under or overscored because amounts can vary widely over quite small areas.

References

BILLING, E. (1974). The effect of temperature on the growth of the fireblight pathogen, *Erwinia amylovora*. *Journal of Applied Bacteriology*, **37**, 643–648.

BILLING, E. (1975). The use of *in vitro* growth rates of *Erwinia amylovora* for predicting fireblight disease activity in the field. *Society for General Microbiology, Proceedings*, **3**, 12 .

BILLING, E. (1976). Weather and fireblight in England. *Annals of Applied Biology*, **82**, 259–266.

BROOKS, A. N. (1926). Studies on the epidemiology and control of fireblight of apple. *Phytopathology*, **16**, 665–696.

CROSSE, J. E., GOODMAN, R. N. & SHAFFER, W. H. (1972). Leaf damage as a predisposing factor in the infection of apple shoots by *Erwinia amylovora*. *Phytopathology*, **62**, 176–182.

EDEN-GREEN, S. J. (1972). Studies in fireblight disease of apple, pear and hawthorn (*Erwinia amylovora* (Burrill) Winslow *et al.*). Ph.D. Thesis, University of London.

GOODE, J. E. (1975). Water storage, water stress and crop responses to irrigation. In *Climate and the orchard*. (Pereira, H. C., ed.). pp. 51–62.

LUEPSCHEN, N. S., PARKER, K. G. & MILLS, W. D. (1961). Five year study of fireblight blossom infection and its control in New York. *Cornell Agricultural Experimental Station Bulletin*, **963**, 1–19.

MILLS, W. D. (1955). Fireblight development on apple in Western New York. *Plant Disease Reporter*, **39**, 206–207.

POWELL, D. (1965). Factors influencing the severity of fireblight infections on apple and pear. *Michigan State Horticultural Society Annual Meeting*, **94**, 1–7.

Addendum

Since this paper was prepared, the system has been tested further and, as suspected (p. 54), the moisture index (R) needs adjustment during the spring blossom period.

It is now assumed that moisture is not a limiting factor for multiplication until late May and, when calculating I periods, R is now scored as 1·0 daily until 21 May regardless of rainfall.

The definition of an infection day remains the same but during spring blossom periods up to 5 June, any day when the PD score is 9·0 or more is counted as an infection day. On such a day, R is scored as 1·0 but only for the purpose of calculating the subsequent I period in question.

This adjustment proved necessary in the light of experience. It may reflect the likelihood that pollinating insects would be highly active on such days and likely to spread infection. In addition, both plant and bacterial growth would be near maximal under these conditions (if soil moisture was not a limiting factor) and establishment of infection might be particularly rapid.

Additional Reference

BILLING, E. (1978). Development in fireblight prediction in south-east England. In *Plant disease epidemiology* (Scott, P. R. & Bainbridge, A., eds). Oxford: Blackwells Scientific Publications Ltd, pp. 159–166.

Spiroplasmas and other Micro-organisms Causing Yellows Diseases of Plants

M. J. Daniels, P. G. Markham and R. Townsend

John Innes Institute, Colney Lane, Norwich, Norfolk, England

Plants in all parts of the world are affected by diseases belonging to the so-called "yellows" group, which are believed to be caused by prokaryotic organisms resembling mycoplasmas (or, in a few cases, rickettsias). Infected plants show characteristic symptoms, including yellowing and bronzing of foliage and severe growth abnormalities such as proliferation of axillary shoots, shortening of internodes, reduction of leaf area and morphological changes in floral parts, leading to sterility. These symptoms have given rise to the descriptive names of many of the diseases, such as yellows, yellow-leaf, proliferation, witches' broom, decline, stunt, dwarf, little-leaf, greening, virescence, green petal and phyllody.

Yellows diseases are not transmissible to plants by mechanical inoculation, but they can be transmitted by grafting diseased material to healthy plants or by using the parasitic plant, dodder (*Cuscuta* spp.), as a vector. Infection is spread naturally by insect vectors. Where the vectors are known they are usually leafhoppers, although in a few cases psyllids and planthoppers are responsible. The diseases have long incubation periods in the insects, which are then infective for life. However, the infection is not passed transovarially to succeeding generations.

Until about ten years ago the yellows diseases were assumed to be caused by viruses, but the appearance of the first of many papers showing by electron microscopy the presence of mycoplasma-like bodies in the sieve tubes of diseased plants, together with the observation that plants could be at least temporarily cured by tetracycline administration, forced a reappraisal of this view. Today it is generally agreed that organisms resembling mycoplasmas are the aetiological agents of yellows diseases, but proof has been obtained in only two cases to date, citrus stubborn (little-leaf) and corn stunt. To satisfy Koch's postulates it is necessary to cultivate the mycoplasma *in vitro* from diseased plants, to reintroduce it into healthy plants, which must then show the appropriate disease symptoms and finally to reisolate the organism from these plants.

It is the unsolved problem of cultivation of most of the organisms which has hindered progress.

It is convenient to group the presumed agents of yellows diseases as listed.

Spiroplasmas

A mycoplasma-like organism cultured from citrus stubborn-diseased material by Saglio *et al.* (1971) and Fudl-Allah *et al.* (1971) turned out to be a motile, helical filament similar to bodies previously seen in sap expressed from corn stunt diseased plants, and termed "spiroplasmas" by Davis and Worley (1973). The citrus stubborn organism was characterized by Saglio *et al.* (1973) and named *Spiroplasma citri*. It was shown to be a plant pathogen by Daniels *et al.* (1973), and to be the agent of citrus stubborn disease by Markham *et al.* (1974).

For some years the corn stunt spiroplasma defied attempts to culture it, but Williamson and Whitcomb (1975) and Chen and Liao (1975) simultaneously succeeded, and showed that the cultured spiroplasmas caused corn-stunt disease when introduced by insects into healthy maize plants. The corn stunt spiroplasma has some serological relationship to *S. citri*, but has yet to be fully characterized.

Recently, Kondo *et al.* (1976) cultured a spiroplasma from *Opuntia tuna monstrosa*, but nothing is yet known about the identity or pathogenicity of this isolate.

It is often possible to discern the helical shape of spiroplasmas in electron micrographs of diseased plants, particularly if rather thick sections (200–300 nm) are cut (Fig. 1).

Mycoplasmas

In the case of most yellows diseases electron micrographs of plant sections show no evidence of helical filaments, the organisms being irregular round bodies about 0·3–0·5 μm in diameter, similar in appearance to many animal mycoplasmas. None of this group of plant pathogens has yet been cultured *in vitro*. Some attempts have been made to purify the micro-organisms from diseased plants using virological techniques such as differential centrifugation (Sinha, 1974) but little is yet known of their properties.

It should be noted that under some conditions, for reasons which are not understood, spiroplasmas may present a similar appearance to mycoplasmas, particularly in insects. A corollary of this is that some pathogens at present classified as mycoplasmas on morphological grounds may eventually turn out to be spiroplasmas.

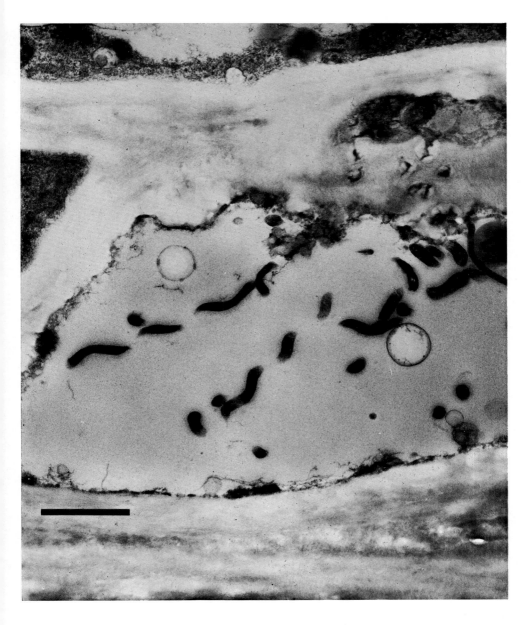

FIG. 1. Electron micrograph of a section (200 nm thick) of phloem tissue of a broad bean plant infected with *Spiroplasma citri* showing the spiroplasmas in a sieve tube. The bar represents 1 μm.

Rickettsia-like Organisms

The organisms associated with about twelve yellows diseases resemble Gram-negative bacteria in having outer layers in addition to the plasma membrane. Moreover they are sensitive to penicillin, which mycoplasmas and spiroplasmas are not. Because of their appearance in thin sections and because they have not yet been cultured they are often referred to, somewhat prematurely, as "rickettsia-like organisms". There are two sub-groups; members of one being found in the phloem of diseased plants and spread probably by leafhoppers, and the other in the xylem, and spread by xylem-feeding insects (frog-hoppers). In some cases the diseases are passed through the egg of the vector to succeeding generations of insects.

The following sections give details of experimental procedures which have been found useful in studies of spiroplasmas. In addition, many of the standard methods used for animal mycoplasmas are readily applicable and are described by Fallon and Whittlestone (1969).

The Culture of Spiroplasmas

Preparation of the inoculum

It is often desirable to surface sterilize plant material, particularly if collected in the field, before attempting to culture spiroplasmas. Sterilization may be achieved by wetting with 70% (v/v) ethanol, immersion in 1% sodium hypochlorite solution for 15 min followed by copious washing with sterile water.

The specimen is ground in a sterile mortar with a small quantity of growth medium and the extract transferred to a centrifuge tube and spun at low speed (e.g. 500 g for 1 min) to remove plant debris. The supernatant is fluid then passed through a sterile Millipore filter Type HA, 0·45 μm pore diameter, in a Swinney syringe adaptor. HA membrane filters retain all but the smallest bacteria so it is safe to omit surface sterilization where the plant is not heavily contaminated, for example when it has been raised in a glasshouse.

Spiroplasmas may be cultured from infected leafhoppers using similar methods. The insects are anaesthetized with carbon dioxide, ground in medium, and the extract filtered. Surface sterilization should not be undertaken because of the risk that the sterilizing agents may penetrate the insect tissues and kill the spiroplasmas.

Growth media and incubation conditions

Spiroplasma citri is usually grown in the medium devised by Saglio *et al.* (1971). This consists of a basal medium containing

PPLO broth (without crystal violet) (Difco)	21 g
Tryptone (Difco)	10 g
Sorbitol	70 g
Fructose	1 g
Glucose	1 g
Sucrose	10 g
Phenol red	20 mg
Distilled water	700 ml.

After autoclaving (120°, 20 min^{-1}) the medium is supplemented with the following sterile additives: horse serum (200 ml), fresh (5% w/v) yeast extract (100 ml), thallous acetate (10 ml of a 2·5% w/v solution) and penicillin G (10^6 units).

For solid media PPLO broth can be replaced by Difco PPLO agar (34 g), or plain agar (10 g) can be added to the basal medium before autoclaving. The molten medium is cooled to 50° before adding the serum, etc.

The above medium can be simplified and we normally use "T" medium containing only PPLO broth (21 g litre^{-1}), sorbitol (70 g litre^{-1}), fructose (1 g litre^{-1}) and horse serum (20% v/v). Wellcome No. 3 Horse Serum (Wellcome Reagents Ltd, Beckenham, Kent, England) is generally satisfactory, although certain batches cause spiroplasmas to clump. The serum may be heated (60° 30 min^{-1}) before use, minimizing the possibility of mycoplasma contamination of cultures.

Spiroplasma citri cultures should be incubated at 32°. The permissible range for growth is from 27 to 35°. The doubling time during exponential growth is about 6 hours and the maximum titre may reach 10^9 colony forming units ml^{-1}. Acid production causes the pH of the medium to fall from the initial value of 7·5 to less than 5 in the course of a few days, and viability then declines rapidly. Plates may be incubated aerobically, but somewhat better growth is obtained in a candle jar or in an atmosphere of 95% N_2 + 5% CO_2. It is often necessary to incubate plates for 1–2 weeks and precautions must be taken to prevent the agar drying, for example by taping the plates or putting a dish of water in the incubator to saturate the atmosphere.

The Corn Stunt Spiroplasma

Chen and Liao (1975) used medium C-3

199 Medium (Gibco)	1 ml
Schneider's Drosophila Medium (Gibco)	0·5 ml
CMRL 1066 Medium (Gibco)	0·5 ml
PPLO broth (Difco)	1·5 g
Sucrose	16 g
Fresh yeast extract	10 ml
Horse serum	20 ml
Phenol red	1 mg
Water	to 100 ml.

Solid media contain 0·8 w/v Oxoid Ionagar No. 2

Liao and Chen (1975) have since reported that a medium containing only PPLO broth (1·5 g), sucrose (16 g), horse serum (20 ml) and water (74 ml) is satisfactory.

Williamson and Whitcomb (1975) used medium M1 containing 2 volumes of Schneider's Drosophila Medium supplemented with Bacto-Peptone (0·5%) and foetal bovine serum (20%) and 1 volume of *S. citri* medium (Saglio *et al.*, 1971) with foetal bovine serum in place of horse serum. Phenol red (50 μg ml^{-1}) and penicillin (1000 U ml^{-1}) are also added. Solid media contain 1·67 or 2·1% (w/v) Noble agar.

We use "T" medium supplemented with 2-oxo-glutarate (100 μg ml^{-1}), and containing 10% (v/v) horse or foetal bovine serum previously dialysed against 1·15% (w/v) KCl. Cultures are incubated at 29°.

The Opuntia tuna monstrosa *Spiroplasma*

Kondo *et al.* (1976) used a medium similar to that of Saglio *et al.* (1971) except that the sorbitol concentration was reduced to 5% (w/v). Cultures were incubated at 25°.

Detection and measurement of growth

Solid media

Spiroplasmas, in common with other mycoplasmas, form small colonies about 0·2 mm in diameter usually having the so-called "fried egg" appearance. This is caused by the organisms growing down into the agar. The periphery of the colony has a "rough" appearance which is believed to be caused by spiroplasmas migrating through the agar and forming satellite microcolonies. A non-motile (and non-helical) strain of *S. citri* described by Townsend *et al.* (1977) gives smooth colonies.

Colonies may be stained with Dienes' stain (Fallon and Whittlestone, 1969). When it is necessary to count colonies, for example in determining the viable count of a culture, it is convenient to fix and stain the colonies with Dienes' stain diluted 20-fold in ethanol (Scriba, 1968). The agar, but not the colonies, may be decolorized by exhaustive washing with water (Fig. 2).

Liquid media

1. Acid production during growth of fermentative species (including spiroplasmas) causes the phenol red indicator to change colour from red to yellow as the pH falls from 7·5 to less than 5. Subsequently the pH may rise owing to release of ammonia from arginine (Townsend, 1976). However, by the time such colour changes are apparent the phase of active growth is almost over.
2. Marked turbidity is often seen in spiroplasma cultures, caused in part by clumps of cells and in part by precipitated medium components. Measurement of turbidity is therefore an unreliable indicator of growth.
3. Spiroplasmas possess a characteristic morphology and motility which makes them easy to detect with the light microscope, preferably using dark field illumination (Davis and Worley, 1973; Cole *et al.*, 1973). Actively growing cultures contain predominantly short, helical filaments, whereas older cultures in the stationary phase of growth show a preponderance of long non-helical filaments with bulbous protuberances. Finally the cells degenerate into small round bodies which are probably non-viable.
4. Smears from liquid cultures or touch preparations from colonies may be air-dried, fixed with methanol and stained with Giemsa stain (Fallon and Whittlestone, 1969) for examination by brightfield microscopy. It is not usually possible to preserve the helicity of filaments during this procedure.
5. Samples may be examined by electron microscopy, either as whole amounts negatively stained with ammonium molybdate or as thin sections after fixing and embedding in resins. Suitable techniques are described by Cole *et al.* (1973).
6. The presence of pathogenic organisms can be demonstrated by injecting samples into insects as described below.
7. Quantitative measurements of growth make use of viable counting procedures, incorporation of radioactive precursors into macromolecules or chemical measurements of cell constituents.

The small size of spiroplasma colonies makes them ideally suited to a viable counting method similar to that of Miles and Misra (1938). Serial

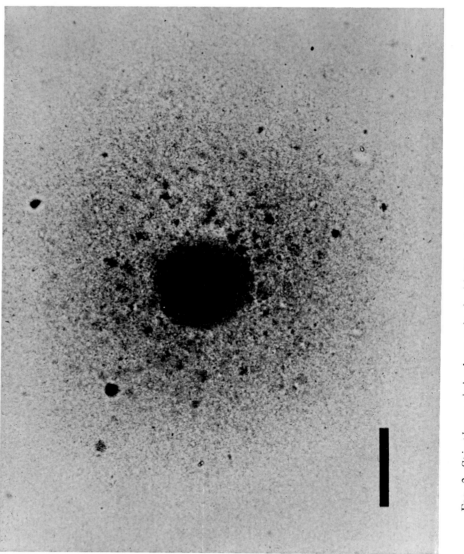

FIG. 2. *Spiroplasma citri* colony stained with Dienes' stain. The bar represents 0·1 mm.

dilutions are best made using complete growth medium as a diluent. Drops of about 10 μl are placed on plates and allowed to soak in. At least six drops can be put on one plate. An automatic pipette with disposable autoclavable tips is ideal for this purpose, for example the "Finnpipette" (Buckley Membranes Ltd, Prestwood, Great Missenden, Bucks, England). It is necessary to incubate plates for at least a week before staining the colonies and counting them.

Radioactive thymidine and amino acids are often used as macromolecular precursors. At intervals samples of 0·1 ml are removed from the culture and added to 2 ml of ice-cold 5 % (w/v) trichloracetic acid (TCA). The mixture is left in ice for about 15 min and the precipitate is then collected by suction on a glass-fibre filter (Whatman type GF/C). The filter is washed 3 times with 5 ml 5 % TCA and once with acetone, dried and transferred to a vial for scintillation counting. It should be noted that if, as is probable, the spiroplasmas are auxotrophic for the precursor substance, and if the specific radioactivity in the medium is constant, then the incorporation is a direct measure of the macromolecular component and hence of the biomass under the prevailing conditions. A necessary consequence is that semi-logarithmic plots of incorporation of different precursors during exponential growth have identical slopes (See Fig. 3; Saglio, 1976).

It is possible to measure chemically some cellular component, for example protein or DNA, on samples of centrifuged cells. A recent method which combines speed and simplicity with sensitivity is the measurement of cellular ATP by a bioluminescence assay (Saglio, 1976; Saglio *et al.*, 1976) (Fig. 3).

Maintenance of cultures

At room temperature or at 4° spiroplasmas survive for 1–2 weeks. Liquid cultures frozen at —20° or better, —70° probably survive for several years, as do lyophilized cultures. The culture medium (complete with serum) is a good medium in which to lyophilize the cells.

The Identification of Cultured Spiroplasmas

Cloning

New isolates should by general agreement be cloned three times. Liquid cultures are filtered through membrane filters of pore diameter 0·45 μm or 0·22 μm and the filtrate plated on agar. A single colony is then picked into broth and when grown the culture is again filtered and plated. The process is repeated once again and a single colony finally selected for propagation. The strain is then referred to (colloquially) as "triply filter-cloned". The filtration steps are designed to eliminate clumps of spiroplasmas and improve the chance that a single colony consists of the progeny of a single spiroplasma filament.

It should be borne in mind that pathogens may be attenuated by successive subculture so it is prudent to store in a frozen state samples of uncloned early passages of all new isolates.

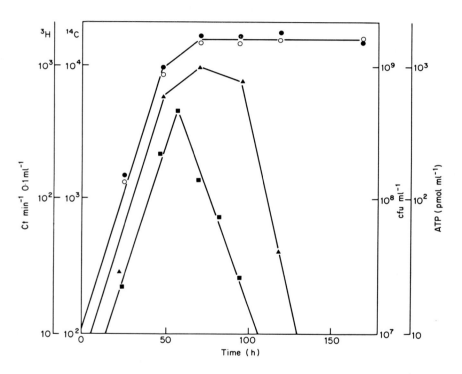

FIG. 3. Growth curve of *Spiroplasma citri* (strain SP-A, NCPPB 2565), in "T" medium at 32°. Measurements were made of colony forming units (cfu) ml^{-1} (▲). Cells were rapidly harvested by vacuum filtration on membrane filters (pore diameter 0·22 μm), ATP was extracted with boiling buffer and measured by a bioluminiscence assay (■). After inoculation of the culture portions were removed and incubated separately with [³H]-phenylalanine (1 mc mmol^{-1}, 5 μc ml^{-1}) or [2-¹⁴C]-thymidine (57 mc mmol^{-1}, 0·5 μc ml^{-1}). At intervals 0·1 ml samples were taken for measurement of incorporated ³H (●) and ¹⁴C (○) (from Saglio, 1976).

Electron microscopy

Examination of electron micrographs of thin sections of organisms is the only definitive test for the absence of a cell wall. Strains should also be examined after subculture for at least 5 transfers in the absence of penicillin or other agents acting on bacterial cell wall synthesis.

Serology

Serological tests are the most important criteria used in identifying mycoplasmas. Many tests have been applied to mycoplasmas and their advantages and disadvantages have been discussed by Freundt (1974). The methods most favoured at present are the growth inhibition test (Clyde, 1964; Black, 1973) in which antiserum applied to paper discs or wells in plates produces a zone of growth inhibition with homologous strains, and the epi-immunofluorescence test applied to colonies on agar (Del Guidice *et al.*, 1967), preferably used in the indirect form. The metabolism inhibition test of Taylor-Robinson *et al.* (1966) is also often used. An additional technique, applicable to spiroplasmas but not other mycoplasmas, is the deformation test, which requires microscopic examination of cultures treated with a range of dilutions of antiserum to detect distortion of the normal helical shape of the organisms. (Williamson and Whitcomb, 1974.)

Biochemical tests

Although spiroplasmas (and mycoplasmas in general) do not show such a range of easily detected biochemical activities as eubacteria, nevertheless certain tests are widely used in characterizing strains. The procedures of Aluotto *et al.* (1970) are usually adopted.

Polyacrylamide gel electrophoresis

Razin and Rottem (1967) showed that the patterns obtained when mycoplasma cell proteins are electrophoresed in polyacrylamide gels are characteristic of the species and the technique is useful for comparing strains. The original procedure in which material is dissolved in phenol and acetic acid has been largely replaced by that described by Daniels and Meddins (1973) in which sodium dodecyl sulphate is used to solubilize the cells. Clearer results can be obtained by using purified membranes rather than whole cells, but the experiments are then more time-consuming.

Characterization of the genome

DNA can be purified from spiroplasmas by the method of Marmur (1961), simplified to the extent that the lack of a cell wall renders lysozyme treatment unnecessary; the harvested cells may be lysed with sodium dodecyl sulphate alone.

The base composition of the purified DNA, expressed as moles % of (guanine + cytosine), abbreviated to % (G + C), can be deduced from measurements of buoyant density in caesium chloride (Schildkraut *et al.*, 1962), or thermal denaturation temperature (Marmur and Doty, 1962).

The haploid genome size is calculated from kinetics of renaturation of DNA fragments of known molecular weight (Bak *et al.*, 1969, 1970; Wetmur and Davidson, 1968).

Examples of the application of these techniques to *S. citri* are given by Saglio *et al.* (1973).

Some measure of "genetic relatedness" between strains is afforded by DNA–DNA hybridization experiments. Denatured DNA from one strain is fixed on Millipore filters and is allowed to react with radioactive homologous or heterologous DNA in solution under renaturing conditions (McConaughy *et al.*, 1969; Saglio *et al.*, 1974). The ratio of the radioactivity fixed with heterologous DNA to that with homologous DNA ranges from 1·0 with closely related organisms (e.g. strains of the same species) to 0·02 or less with unrelated species (e.g. *S. citri* compared with (*Mycoplasma mycoides*).

Characterization of new species

Results of the various tests described above may lead the experimenter to suspect that his isolate is a new species. By common consent a new species is not named until it has been deposited in a recognized culture collection and properly described according to the proposals of the Subcommittee on the Taxonomy of *Mycoplasmatales* (1972).

Studies of the Pathogenicity of Spiroplasmas

Although spiroplasmas may be transmitted experimentally from plant to plant by natural vectors, grafting or dodder, *cultured* spiroplasmas can only be introduced into plants using leafhopper vectors as the means of infection. There are no reports of successful mechanical infection of plants such as is often used with viruses, fungi and bacteria. For many years it was thought that yellows disease agents were highly specific for their vectors, each being transmitted by only a small number of leaf-hopper species (see e.g. Maramorosch, 1952). Thus when *S. citri* was cultured the prospects for transmitting cultured organisms to plants and, it was hoped, demonstrating pathogenicity seemed poor since the natural vectors of citrus stubborn disease were unknown. However, we showed that it is possible to use common British leafhopper species as "artificial" vectors to transmit *S. citri* to many plant species, including orange (*Citrus sinensis*), and thereby to satisfy Koch's postulates (Daniels *et al.*, 1973; Markham *et al.*, 1974; Markham and Townsend, 1974). One of the species (*Euscelidius variegatus*) has recently been shown to be also capable of transmitting the corn stunt spiroplasma (Markham *et al.*, 1977).

Insect stocks

Species chosen as artificial vectors should be mainly phloem feeders, have a wide range of host plants, and produce several generations per year.

The leafhoppers *Euscelis plebejus* and *Euscelidius variegatus* are widely distributed in Britain and are known to be suitable for use as vectors of *S. citri*. Somewhat better results are obtained with *E. variegatus*. To establish a colony of insects females must be trapped and caged singly on suitable food plants, e.g. white clover (*Trifolium repens*) for *Euscelis plebejus*, Italian ryegrass (*Lolium multifolium*) for *Euscelidius variegatus*. It is necessary to check that the insects are not carrying yellows or other diseases by observing test and food plants over an extended period for the appearance of symptoms. The progeny of each female are kept in separate cages and allowed to multiply to give colonies. It is desirable that experiments are always performed on insects from the same colony.

Leafhoppers trapped in the wild may be identified with the help of Handbooks for the Identification of British Insects published by the Royal Entomological Society of London, but specimens from colonies which are to be used in experiments should always be submitted for authoritative identification to a recognized centre such as the British Museum (Natural History).

Microinjection of insects

The apparatus used is illustrated in Fig. 4A and 4B and consists of an insect holder (similar to that described by Maramorosch and Jernberg, 1970, but with individually sprung arms) mounted on the stage of a binocular microscope (magnification about 15 ×), together with a peristaltic pump connected to a foot-operated switch. The needles used for injection are hand-drawn from pyrex glass tubing (4 mm o.d., 2 mm i.d.).

8 cm lengths are drawn out to about a third of the original diameter in a hot gas flame and the drawing of the needle is completed in an alcohol flame, the tip being broken so as to give an orifice of 10–20 μm i.d. The needles are sterilized in an oven before use.

A convenient number of insects are trapped with a pooter and removed from the colony. After having been anaesthetized by passing carbon

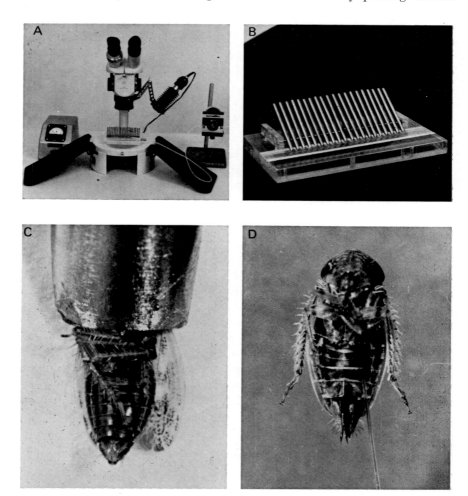

FIG. 4. Apparatus for microinjection of leafhoppers. A, complete apparatus; B, multiple insect holder; C, anaesthetized leafhopper in insect holder ready for injection; D, leafhopper being injected with a glass needle (for clarity the insect was removed from the holder before the photograph was taken).

dioxide into the bottle they are placed dorsal side down in the insect holder (Fig. 4c). The inoculum of spiroplasma culture is put in the glass needle which is connected to a polythene tube passing through the pump rollers. The pump is adjusted to give a suitable flow rate, but when sufficient pressure has been established it is not necessary for the pump to operate continuously, since the flow rate is largely determined by the bore of the capillary. Insects are injected between a pair of abdominal sternites (Fig. 4d) with about 0·1 μl of the fluid. In the case of *Euscelis plebejus* (length about 3·5 mm) this volume may cause the abdomen to distend slightly.

After injection the insects are caged on food plants until the incubation period (a time when the insects are non-infective) has passed (2–3 weeks), and the survivors (usually 60–90%) are then caged individually or in groups on test plants using plastic cages. After the desired period of inoculation feeding the plants are sprayed with a systemic insecticide and left in a glasshouse to permit symptoms to develop.

Insects and plants must be maintained at temperatures of not less than 27° if *S. citri* is to grow and produce clear symptoms. In spiroplasma cultures the maximum growth rate is obtained at 32°, which is also the optimal temperature for symptom expression in infected *Citrus* plants (Olson and Rogers, 1969). The optimal temperature for the corn stunt spiroplasma is somewhat lower, about 29° (Chen and Liao, 1975; Williamson and Whitcomb, 1975).

Membrane feeding

Another method of infecting insects with spiroplasmas is to allow them to feed through membranes of thinly stretched Parafilm M (American Can Co., Greenwich, Ct, USA) into suspensions of spiroplasmas in 5% (w/v) sucrose solution buffered with 0·01 M phosphate buffer pH 7. After feeding for several hours, the insects are removed to plants. Although this method of infecting insects approximates to the natural acquisition process, it appears to be less efficient in rendering the insects infective for plants than the microinjection method.

Infection of plants

The symptoms produced by *S. citri* infection of various plants have been described by Markham and Townsend (1974) and consist in general of chlorosis, dwarfing of new growth and, in several species, sudden wilt followed by death. The symptoms of corn stunt in maize were described by Maramorosch (1955) and Stoner (1964). So far *Vinca rosea* and *Vicia faba* are the only dicotyledons to have been infected with corn stunt (Markham *et al.*, 1977).

If sap from corn stunt infected plants or haemolymph from vector insects are examined with the light microscope using dark field optics, spiroplasmas are easily seen. For reasons which are not fully understood, *S. citri* cannot be detected in insect haemolymph or plant sap by this method.

Spiroplasmas can be detected in electron micrographs of experimentally infected plants. The helical morphology is most easily seen if rather thick sections are cut (200–300 nm) (Davis and Worley, 1973) (Fig. 1). Similar procedures applied to organs of infective insects however fail to reveal helical organisms. In salivary glands spiroplasmas occupy membrane-bounded pockets in cells and appear to be roughly spherical. It is not known why the helical morphology is lost in insect tissues.

Final proof that plants are infected may be obtained by culturing the spiroplasmas and demonstrating that they are identical with those originally injected into the leafhoppers.

Phytotoxin production

Daniels and Meddins (1974) presented evidence that *S. citri* produces a phytotoxin in culture. For the preliminary experiments described a bioassay was used which depended on the inhibition of growth of a unicellular green alga (*Chlorogonium euchlorum*). This assay suffers from the disadvantage that substances in *S. citri* growth medium interfere, and it is therefore only suitable for use with partially purified preparations. To avoid this problem an alternative procedure has been devised using higher plant tissue which can be applied to crude culture fluids.

Young leaves are removed from 2- to 3-week-old seedlings of broad bean (*Vicia faba*), and surface-sterilized by immersion for 30 s in 70% (v/v) ethanol followed by washing several times with sterile water. The lower epidermis is stripped from the leaves and the tissue is then cut into pieces about 3 mm² which are floated on sterile water (stripped surface down) until required. Dilutions of the solution to be assayed together with appropriate controls are prepared and leaf pieces are then taken, blotted briefly on filter paper and floated on the solutions. About 5 pieces of leaf are used for each dilution of each solution. After incubation overnight at 37° the pieces of tissue are fixed and decolorized with methanol. Samples treated with uninoculated *S. citri* medium remain white, whereas those exposed to culture fluids turn black (Fig. 5). Presumably the toxin causes damage to leaf cells, activating the latent polyphenol-oxidase (Kenten, 1958) and causing the deposition of black oxidation

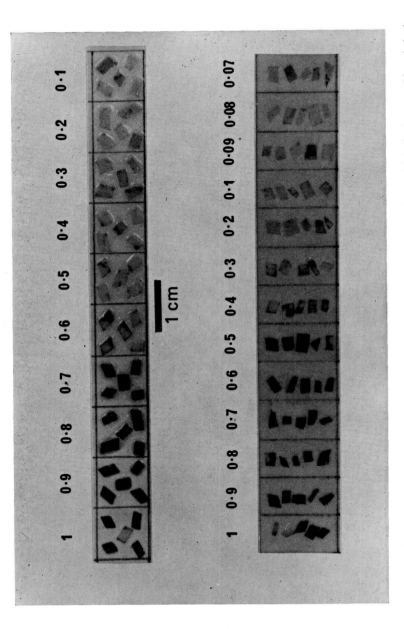

FIG. 5. Bioassay of *Spiroplasma citri* phytotoxin. Pieces of broad bean leaf tissue from which the lower epidermis had been stripped were incubated for 16 h at 37° with *S. citri* culture filtrate diluted with 10% (w/v) sorbitol to give a range of concentrations (relative to undiluted filtrate) shown above each panel. The tissue was subsequently fixed and decolorized with methanol. The end point at which the tissue just fails to turn black is taken to be 0·6 (for the assay shown in the upper panel) and 0·3 (lower panel).

products. Cultures of other mycoplasmas or contaminating bacteria do not cause blackening. The end-point of the assay is taken as that dilution of the solution which just fails to cause blackening. With young leaves the end-point for untreated *S. citri* cultures at the end of exponential growth corresponds to a tenfold dilution, approximately. This assay has been found suitable for comparing toxin production by different strains and for monitoring purification procedures.

Conclusion

If this article has concentrated on spiroplasmas, causing but two of the many yellows diseases, to the virtual exclusion of mycoplasmas and rickettsia-like organisms, it is because our ability to culture spiroplasmas in bacteriological media makes it possible to explore so many aspects of their biology. In contrast the student of plant mycoplasmas and rickettsia-like organisms is restricted to morphological observations of diseased plants and vectors and to transmission experiments (using either natural transmission or microinjection of insects with crude extracts of diseased plants). When mycoplasmas and rickettsia-like organisms are eventually cultured it may be anticipated that the methods used for spiroplasmas will be applicable with little modification. However, it should be borne in mind that the problem of cultivating has been extensively studied in many laboratories and most of the work remains unpublished. As examples of the painstaking unsuccessful attempts which have been made to devise suitable media the papers of Hayflick and Arai (1973) and Caudwell *et al.* (1974) may be cited.

References

ALUOTTO, B. B., WITTLER, R. G., WILLIAMS, C. O. & FABER, J. E. (1970). Standardized bacteriologic techniques for the characterization of *Mycoplasma* species. *International Journal of Systematic Bacteriology*, **20**, 35–58.

BAK, A. L., BLACK, F. T., CHRISTIANSEN, C. & FREUNDT, E. A. (1969). Genome size of mycoplasmal DNA. *Nature, London*, **224**, 1209–1210.

BAK, A. L., CHRISTIANSEN, C. & STENDERUP, A. (1970). Bacterial genome sizes determined by DNA renaturation studies. *Journal of General Microbiology*, **64**, 377–380.

BLACK, F. T. (1973). Modification of the growth inhibition test and its application to human T-mycoplasmas. *Applied Microbiology*, **25**, 528–533.

CAUDWELL, A., KUSZALA, C. & LARRUE, J. (1974). Sur la culture *in vitro* des agents infectieux responsables des jaunisses des plantes (MLO). *Annales de Phytopathologie*, **6**, 173–190.

CHEN, T. A. & LIAO, C. H. (1975). Corn stunt spiroplasma: isolation, cultivation, and proof of pathogenicity. *Science*, **188**, 1015–1017.

CLYDE, W. A. (1964). Mycoplasma species identification based upon growth inhibition by specific antisera. *Journal of Immunology*, **92**, 958–965.

COLE, R. M., TULLY, J. G., POPKIN, T. J. & BOVÉ, J. M. (1973). Morphology, ultrastructure and bacteriophage infection of the helical mycoplasma-like organism (*Spiroplasma citri* gen. nov., sp. nov.) cultured from "stubborn" disease of citrus. *Journal of Bacteriology*, **115**, 367–386.

DANIELS, M. J. & MEDDINS, B. M. (1973). Polyacrylamide gel electrophoresis of mycoplasma proteins in sodium dodecyl sulphate. *Journal of General Microbiology*, **76**, 239–242.

DANIELS, M. J. & MEDDINS, B. M. (1974). The pathogenicity of *Spiroplasma citri*. *Les Colloques de l'Institut National de la Santé et de la Recherche Médicale*, **33**, 195–200.

DANIELS, M. J., MARKHAM, P. G., MEDDINS, B. M., PLASKITT, A. K., TOWNSEND, R. & BAR-JOSEPH, M. (1973). Axenic culture of a plant pathogenic spiroplasma. *Nature, London*, **244**, 523–524.

DAVIS, R. E. & WORLEY, J. F. (1973). Spiroplasma: motile, helical microorganism associated with corn stunt disease. *Phytopathology*, **63**, 403–408.

DEL GIUDICE, R. A., ROBILLARD, N. F. & CARSKI, T. R. (1967). Immunofluorescence identification of *Mycoplasma* on agar by use of incident illumination. *Journal of Bacteriology*, **93**, 1205–1209.

FALLON, R. J. & WHITTLESTONE, P. (1969). Isolation, cultivation and maintenance of mycoplasmas. In *Methods in Microbiology*, Vol. 3B (Norris, J. R. & Ribbons, D. W., eds). London and New York: Academic Press, p. 241.

FREUNDT, E. A. (1974). Practical aspects of serological identification. *Les Colloques de l'Institut National de la Santé et de la Recherche Médicale*, **33**, 161–168.

FUDL-ALLAH, A. E-S., CALAVAN, E. C. & IGWEGBE, E. C. K. (1971). Culture of a mycoplasmalike organism associated with stubborn disease of citrus. *Phytopathology*, **61**, 1321.

HAYFLICK, L. & ARAI, S. (1973). Failure to isolate mycoplasmas from aster yellows-diseased plants and leafhoppers. *Annals of the New York Academy of Sciences*, **225**, 494–502.

KENTEN, R. H. (1958). Latent phenolase in extracts of broad bean (*Vicia faba* L.) leaves. *Biochemical Journal*, **68**, 244–251.

KONDO, F., MCINTOSH, A. H., PADHI, S. B. & MARAMOROSCH, K. (1976). A spiroplasma isolated from the ornamental cactus *Opuntia tuna monstrosa*. *Proceedings of the Society of General Microbiology*, **3**, 154.

LIAO, C. H. & CHEN, T. A. (1975). A simple medium for the isolation and cultivation of corn stunt spiroplasma. *Proceedings of the American Phytopathological Society*, **2**, 100.

MCCONAUGHY, B. L., LAIRD, C. D. & MCCARTHY, B. J. (1969). Nucleic acid reassociation in formamide. *Biochemistry, New York*, **8**, 3289–3295.

MARAMOROSCH, K. (1952). Studies on the nature of the specific transmission of aster-yellows and corn-stunt viruses. *Phytopathology*, **42**, 663–668.

MARAMOROSCH, K. (1955). The occurrence of two distinct types of corn stunt in Mexico. *Plant Disease Reporter*, **39**, 896–898.

MARAMOROSCH, K. & JERNBERG, N. (1970). An adjustable multiple-insect holder for microinjection. *Journal of Economic Entomology*, **63**, 1216–1218.

MARKHAM, P. G. & TOWNSEND, R. (1974). Transmission of *Spiroplasma citri* to plants. *Les Colloques de l'Institut National de la Santé et de la Recherche Médicale*, **33**, 201–206.

MARKHAM, P. G., TOWNSEND, R., BAR-JOSEPH, M., DANIELS, M. J., PLASKITT, A. & MEDDINS, B. M. (1974). Spiroplasmas are the causal agents of citrus little-leaf disease. *Annals of Applied Biology*, **78**, 49–57.

MARKHAM, P. G., TOWNSEND, R., PLASKITT, K. & SAGLIO, P. (1977). Transmission of corn stunt to dicotyledonous plants. *Plant Disease Reporter*, **61**, 342–345.

MARMUR, J. (1961). A procedure for the isolation of deoxyribonucleic acid from microorganisms. *Journal of Molecular Biology*, **3**, 208–218.

MARMUR, J. & DOTY, P. (1962). Determination of the base composition of deoxyribonucleic acid from its thermal denaturation temperature. *Journal of Molecular Biology*, **5**, 109–118.

MILES, A. A. & MISRA, S. S. (1938). The estimation of the bactericidal power of blood. *Journal of Hygiene, Cambridge*, **38**, 732–749.

OLSON, E. O. & ROGERS, B. (1969). Effect of temperature on expression and transmission of stubborn disease of citrus. *Plant Disease Reporter*, **53**, 45–49.

RAZIN, S. & ROTTEM, S. (1967). Identification of *Mycoplasma* and other microorganisms by polyacrylamide-gel electrophoresis of cell proteins. *Journal of Bacteriology*, **94**, 1807–1810.

SAGLIO, P. (1976). ATP and energetic charge as criteria of growth and metabolic activity of Mollicutes: application to *Spiroplasma citri*. *Sixty sixth Annual Report, John Innes Institute, Norwich*, 90–91.

SAGLIO, P., LAFLÉCHE, D., BONISSOL, C. & BOVÉ, J. M. (1971). Isolement et culture *in vitro* des mycoplasmas associés au "stubborn" des agrumes et leur observation au microscope électronique. *Comptes Rendus Hebdomadaires des Séances de l'Academie des Sciences. Paris Série D*, **272**, 1387–1390.

SAGLIO, P., LHOSPITAL, M., LAFLÉCHE, D., DUPONT, G., BOVÉ, J. M., TULLY, J. G. & FREUNDT, E. A. (1973). *Spiroplasma citri* gen. and sp. n.: a mycoplasma-like organism associated with "stubborn" disease of citrus. *International Journal of Systematic Bacteriology*, **23**, 191–204.

SAGLIO, P., DAVIS, R. E., DALIBART, R., DUPONT, G. & BOVÉ, J. M. (1974). *Spiroplasma citri*: L'espèce type des spiroplasmas. *Les Colloques de l'Institut National de la Santé et de la Recherche Médicale*, **33**, 27–34.

SAGLIO, P., DANIELS, M. J. & PRADET, A. (1976). ATP and energy charge as criteria of growth and metabolic activity of mollicutes: application to *Spiroplasma citri*. *Proceedings of the Society for General Microbiology*, **3**, 155.

SCHILDKRAUT, C. L., MARMUR, J. & DOTY, P. (1962). Determination of the base composition of deoxyribonucleic acid from its buoyant density in CsCl. *Journal of Molecular Biology*, **4**, 430–443.

SCRIBA, M. (1968). Studies to eliminate mycoplasma contamination in cell cultures with the aid of antibiotics. *Zeitschrift für Medizinische Mikrobiologie und Immunologie*, **154**, 267–276.

SINHA, R. C. (1974). Purification of mycoplasma-like organisms from China aster plants affected with clover phyllody. *Phytopathology*, **64**, 1156–1158.

STONER, W. N. (1964). Corn stunt disease in the United States through 1963. *Plant Disease Reporter*, **48**, 640–644.

Subcommittee on the Taxonomy of *Mycoplasmatales* (1972). International Committee on Systematic Bacteriology, Proposal for minimal standards for descriptions of new species of the order *Mycoplasmatales*. *International Journal of Systematic Bacteriology*, **22**, 184–188.

TAYLOR-ROBINSON, D., PURCELL, R. H., WONG, D. C. & CHANOCK, R. M.

(1966). Colour test for the measurement of antibody to certain *Mycoplasma* species based upon the inhibition of acid production. *Journal of Hygiene, Cambridge,* **64**, 91–104.

TOWNSEND, R. (1976). Arginine metabolism by *Spiroplasma citri. Journal of General Microbiology,* **94**, 417–420.

TOWNSEND, R., MARKHAM, P. G., PLASKITT, K. A. & DANIELS, M. J. (1977). Isolation and characterization of a non-helical strain of *Spiroplasma citri. Journal of General Microbiology,* **100**, 15–21.

WETMUR, J. G. & DAVIDSON, N. (1968). Kinetics of renaturation of DNA. *Journal of Molecular Biology,* **31**, 349–370.

WILLIAMSON, D. L. & WHITCOMB, R. F. (1974). Helical, wall-free prokaryotes in Drosophila, leafhoppers and plants. *Les Colloques de l'Institut National de la Santé et de la Recherche Médicale,* **33**, 283–290.

WILLIAMSON, D. L. & WHITCOMB, R. F. (1975). Plant mycoplasmas: a cultivable spiroplasma causes corn stunt disease. *Science,* **188**, 1018–1020.

Barley Mildew Infection Periods

R. W. POLLEY

Ministry of Agriculture, Fisheries and Food, Plant Pathology Laboratory, Hatching Green, Harpenden, Hertfordshire, England

The criteria for a "high-risk period" are designed to detect days on which there is a high risk of large numbers of mildew spores being released in spring barley crops (Polley and King, 1973).

When used to determine the most likely best spray date in terms of yield, the criteria should be used in conjunction with an observation of mildew level in the crop which should be 3–5% on the lower leaves before a spray is applied. (Jenkins and Storey, 1975).

The following parameters are used to determine the occurrence of a "high-risk period"

1.	day maximum temperature	$>15\cdot6°$
2.	day sunshine	>5 hours
3.	day rainfall	<1 mm
4.	day run-of-wind	>246 km.

If data from synoptic stations are to be used, then the day run-of-wind record can be replaced by the highest of the four wind speed recordings taken at the main synoptic hours, 0000, 0600, 1200 and 1800 GMT. The critical value for this factor is >15 knots.

The following rules are applied to the criteria in order to define "high-risk periods" (see Table 1).

1. A "high-risk day" is one on which all four factors have been satisfied, or the second consecutive day when 3 of the factors have been satisfied, or the third consecutive day on which at least two factors have been satisfied with one or two of those days having had 3 factors satisfied.

2. A "high-risk day" denotes the start of a "high-risk period" which is terminated by a day when none or one of the factors has been satisfied or the third consecutive day when only two factors have been satisfied.

R. W. POLLEY

TABLE 1. Typical "high risk periods" during the month of May

Date	Number of Factors Satisfied				
May 1	0	4	2	0	1
2	1	3	2	4	0
3	2	2	1	2	3
4	3	2	3	2	3
5	2	3	2	2	2
6	2	2	3	1	2
7	4	2	1	3	2
8	2	2	2	1	4
9	0	3	3	4	3
10	1	4	4	1	1
11	3	1	3	2	0
12	1	0	1	2	2

⊤, "High risk period".

An alternative method for detecting "high-risk days" is by use of the Smith Index (Polley and Smith, 1973). This involves the calculation of an index equal to $3T + \frac{1}{2}W + S$ where T is day maximum temperature in °, W is wind speed in knots at 1200 h and S is hours of sunshine. Critical days occur when the value of this index exceeds 64, but a spray should be applied during critical periods only if the mildew level in the crop has reached 3–5 % on the lower leaves.

ADAS advisers are informed of the occurrence of "high-risk periods" and Smith Index Days throughout the growing season by the Meteorological Office.

References

JENKINS, J. E. E. & STOREY, I. F. (1975). Influence of spray timing for the control of powdery mildew on the yield of spring barley. *Plant Pathology*, **24**, 125–134.

POLLEY, R. W. & KING, J. E. (1973). A preliminary proposal for the detection of barley mildew infection periods. *Plant Pathology*, **22**, 11–16.

POLLEY, R. W. & SMITH, L. P. (1973). Barley mildew forecasting. *Proceedings of the 7th British Insecticide and Fungicide Conference*, 373–378.

Ecological Studies on *Rhizobium trifolii* Using Marker Techniques for Strain Identification

D. Gareth Jones and E. S. P. Bromfield

Department of Agricultural Botany, University College of Wales, Aberystwyth, Wales

Aspects of the ecology of *Rhizobium trifolii* were studied utilizing genetic markers (Obaton, 1971; Schwinghamer and Dudman, 1972) to identify strains in root nodules and as free-living bacteria. Additional strain identification methods were used in some experiments and these included the fluorescent antibody technique (FAT) (Trinick, 1969; Jones and Russell, 1972; Schmidt, 1973) and absorption of congo red by an ineffective strain on solid medium.

The competitive ability, in terms of nodules produced, of selected symbiotically effective doubly labelled streptomycin/spectinomycin-resistant mutants relative to their wild type parent strains was investigated using an ineffective strain to provide the competitive factor. The antibiotic-resistant mutants so examined were found to be inferior to the wild type parents in nodulating competitiveness, although the variation observed between mutants in this property indicated that improvement should be possible by selection. Nodules were typed using the FAT, genetic markers and a congo red-containing medium on which it was possible to recognize the ineffective strain. Application of these techniques also enabled the frequency of double strain occupancy of nodules to be determined (Table 1).

In another experiment the incidence of doubly infected nodules containing streptomycin- and spectinomycin-resistant strains was found to be very much lower when three clover varieties were grown in soil than when cultured under aseptic tube conditions. Furthermore, none of the eighteen nodule isolates analysed from plants grown in soil consisted of both indigenous and mutant strains as detected by the replica plating method.

The data also provided evidence for differences in competitive ability for nodulation of the antibiotic-resistant mutants and for a clover host effect on the nodulating success of the streptomycin-resistant strain

TABLE 1. The results of inoculating white clover with pure strains of *Rhizobium* (wild types and antibiotic resistant mutants) and mixtures 1 : 10 effective strains : ineffective strain (Coryn)

Strain number and label sequence	% effective viable cells in inoculum[a] (intended ratio 1:10 effective : ineffective)	% singly infected effective nodules[b] (mixed inoculation treatments)	% doubly infected nodules[b]	Mean dry weight plant-1 (mg) (log transformation) (mixed inoculation treatments)	Mean dry weight plant-1 (mg) (log transformation) (pure inoculation treatments)
32	9·0	61·0	18·0	2·07	2·49
32 *Str/Spc**	26·0	34·0	20·0	1·49	2·29
32 *Spc/Str*	11·0	31·0	22·0	1·51	2·33
A21111	9·0	28·0	10·0	1·59	2·32
A121111 *Str/Spc*	10·0	16·0	5·0	1·34	2·08
A121111 *Spc/Str*	8·0	5·0	1·0	1·13	1·61
7A	7·0	23·0	8·0	1·56	2·45
7A *Str/Spc*	9·0	5·0	6·0	1·16	1·75

Str: streptomycin;

Spc: spectinomycin strains resistant to 150/150 *Spc/Str* or *Str/Spc* (μg/ml).

[a] Determined using congo red absorption technique to distinguish Coryn strain from non-dye absorbing effective strains.

[b] Results from typing over 1000 nodules using the fluorescent antibody technique, genetic markers and differential absorption of congo red.

Mean dry weight plant⁻¹ (mg) of Coryn inoculated plants = *1·14*.

Mean dry weight plant⁻¹ (mg) of uninoculated control plants = *1·10*.

"D" at 5% = 0·36 (D calculated from Q in the studentized range).

TABLE 2. The percentage of singly and doubly infected nodules on three clover varieties inoculated with two antibiotic-resistant strains of *R. trifolii* in pure inocula and in a 1:1 mixture

Inoculum / Nodule type or variety	Agar culture 1:1 Mixture						Soil				
			Doubles	1:1 Mixture			Doubles	32 Spc		7A Str	
	32Spc*	7AStr*	(7AStr +32Spc)	32Spc	7AStr	Indigenous	(7AStr +32Spc)	32Spc	Idigenous	7AStr	Indigenous
S 184	50·0	25·0	25·0	29·6	0	69·4	1·0	75·0	25·0	7·5	92·5
S 100	59·3	15·3	25·4	35·6	0	64·4	0	62·5	37·5	22·5	77·5
S 123	76·6	6·4	17·0	32·0	0	68·0	0	66·7	33·3	2·5	97·5

$\chi^2 = 7·41$ p <0·05
d.o.f. = 2
(excluding doubles)
Results from typing c.150 nodules

$\chi^2 = 0·76$ N.S.
d.o.f. = 2
Results from typing c.300 nodules

$\chi^2 = 1·49$ N.S.
d.o.f. = 2
Results from typing c.150 nodules

$\chi^2 = 8·97$ p <0·05
d.o.f. = 2
Results from typing c.150 nodules

"D" at 1% = 0·41.

Str: streptomycin; *Spc*: spectinomycin strains resistant to 250 μg ml^{-1} *Str* or *Spc*.

(Table 2). These results were in agreement with previous work utilizing the FAT for strain identification (Russell and Jones, 1975a, 1975b).

An investigation concerning the survival of genetically marked *Rhizobium* strains in acid soils was also carried out. Two streptomycin-resistant mutants were selected from strains screened for acid tolerance on a citrate-phosphate buffered agar medium and then evaluated for persistency in three acid upland soils using a selective medium based on that described by Danso and Alexander (1974). Strain 7A *Str* was superior to strain 16 *Str* in persistency in all three soils whether limed or unlimed. Strain 16 *Str* was also found to be a more prolific acid producer on Norris (1965) medium than strain 7A *Str* and thus might be considered to have aggravated the already acid environment.

Genetically marked strains were also used to investigate the possibility of their adaptation to acid soils. Streptomycin-resistant mutants were introduced into acid soils for intervals of time and after reisolation the performance in terms of survival of "trained" isolates was compared to the original, untrained isolates by re-introduction into the soils. The method of strain identification was successful although no evidence for adaptation was found.

References

DANSO, S. K. A. & ALEXANDER, M. (1974). Survival of two strains of *Rhizobium* in soil. *Soil Science Society of America, Proceedings*, **38**, 86–89.

JONES, D. GARETH & RUSSELL, P. E. (1972). The application of immunofluorescence techniques to host plant/nodule bacteria selectivity experiments using *Trifolium repens*. *Soil Biology and Biochemistry*, **4**, 277–282.

NORRIS, D. (1965). Acid production by Rhizobium. A unifying concept. *Plant and Soil*, **22**, 143–166.

OBATON, M. (1971). Utilisation de mutants spontanés résistants aux antibiotiques pour l'étude écologique des *Rhizobium*. *Compte-rendu de l'Académie des sciences, Paris* Ser. D., **272**, 2630–2633.

RUSSELL, P. E. & JONES, D. GARETH (1975a). Variation in the selection of *Rhizobium trifolii* by varieties of red and white clover. *Soil Biology and Biochemistry*, 15–18.

RUSSELL, P. E. & JONES, D. GARETH (1975b). Immunofluorescence studies of selection of strains of *R. trifolii* by S. 184 white clover (*T. repens L.*) *Plant and Soil*, **42**, 119–129.

SCHMIDT, E. L. (1973). Fluorescent antibody techniques for the study of microbial ecology. *Bulletin Ecological Research Committee* (Stockholm), **17**, 67–76.

SCHWINGHAMER, E. A. & DUDMAN, W. F. (1972). Evaluation of Spectinomycin resistance as a marker for ecological studies with rhizobium spp. *Journal of Applied Bacteriology*, **36**, 263–272.

TRINICK, M. J. (1969). Identification of legume nodule bacteroids by the fluorescent antibody reaction. *Journal of Applied Bacteriology*, **32**, 181–186.

Selective Media for Estimating
Pseudomonas solanacearum in Kenyan Soils

D. C. HARRIS*

East Malling Research Station, Maidstone, Kent, England

For quantitative studies of bacterial plant pathogens in soil the dilution plate has several advantages over other methods, but when the pathogen is outnumbered by other micro-organisms selective media are essential. While investigating the decline of soil populations of a Kenyan strain of *Pseudomonas solanacearum* causing a wilt disease of potato and tomato it was found that a highly selective medium could be obtained by relatively simple modifications to a medium used for differentiating colony types of this species.

When the concentrations of 2,3,5-triphenyltetrazolium chloride (TTC) in Kelman's basal medium supplemented with actidione was increased to 2000 or 4000 mg litre^{-1} the size and number of colonies on soil dilution plates was markedly reduced whilst the growth of *P. solanacearum* was virtually unaffected. Colonies of the pathogen on high TTC formulations of this base were highly distinctive and could be counted directly on dilution plates. Estimates of the pathogen from inoculated soil were close to those expected.

The inclusion of maximum non-inhibitory levels of neomycin, polymyxin, streptomycin or tyrothricin improved the selectivity of the high TTC medium but only marginally in most instances. Ampicillin, chloramphenicol, erythromycin, penicillin, sulphathiazole and tetracycline were of no value for improving its selectivity. With excess antibiotic or with non-inhibitory levels on very crowded plates the colony morphology of the pathogen was modified to a smaller and different, but equally distinctive form. The appearance of this colony type was invariably associated with a reduced recovery of the pathogen.

Using Kelman's base with 4000 mg litre^{-1} TTC, 100 mg litre^{-1} actidione and 200 mg litre^{-1} neomycin it was possible to estimate *P. solanacearum* in naturally infested soils when outnumbered by up to

* Formerly: National Agricultural Laboratories, P.O. Box 30028, Nairobi, Kenya.

3000 to one and at levels as low as 10^2 cells g^{-1} soil. This medium was even more effective with an inoculated compost soil.

References

BUDDENHAGEN, I. W. & KELMAN, A. (1964). Biological and physiological aspects of bacterial wilt caused by *Pseudomonas solanacearum*. *Annual Review of Phytopathology*, **2**, 203–230.

CUPPELS, D. & KELMAN, A. (1974). Evaluation of selective media for isolation of soft-rot bacteria from soil and plant tissue. *Phytopathology*, **64**, 468–475.

HAYWARD, A. C. (1964). Characteristics of *Pseudomonas solanacearum*. *Journal of Applied Bacteriology*, **27**, 265–277.

JENKINS, S. F., MORTON, D. J. & DUKES, P. D. (1967). Comparison of techniques for detection of *Pseudomonas solanacearum* in artificially infested soils. *Phytopathology*, **57**, 25–27.

KARGANILLA, A. D. & BUDDENHAGEN, I. W. (1972). Development of a selective medium for *Pseudomonas solanacearum*. *Phytopathology*, **62**, 1373–1376.

KELMAN, A. (1953). The bacterial wilt caused by *Pseudomonas solanacearum*. *North Carolina Agricultural Experiment Station Technical Bulletin*, **99**.

KELMAN, A. (1954). The relationship of pathogenicity of *Pseudomonas solanacearum* to colony appearance in a tetrazolium medium. *Phytopathology*, **44**, 693–695.

LOVREKOVICH, L. & KLEMENT, Z. (1960). Triphenyltetrazolium chloride tolerance of phytopathogenic bacteria. *Phytopathologische Zeitschrift*, **39**, 129–133.

McCARTER, S. M., DUKES, P. D. & JAWORSKI, C. A. (1969). Vertical distribution of *Pseudomonas solanacearum* in several soils. *Phytopathology*, **59**, 1675–1677.

OKABE, N. (1969). Population changes of *Pseudomonas solanacearum* and soil microorganisms in artificially infested natural field soils. *Bulletin of the Faculty of Agriculture, Shizuoka University*, **19**, 1–29.

ROBINSON, R. A. & RAMOS, A. H. (1964). Bacterial wilt of potatoes in Kenya. *East African Agricultural and Forestry Journal*, **30**, 59–64.

TANAKA, Y. & NODA, N. (1973). Studies on the factors affecting survival of *Pseudomonas solanacearum* E. F. Smith, the causal agent of tobacco wilt disease. *Okayama Tobacco Experiment Station Bulletin*, **32**, 81–94.

Treatment of Irrigation Water by Ultra-violet Radiation

R. P. ADAMS AND I. ROBINSON

Microbiology Department, Agricultural Development and Advisory Service, Woodthorne, Wolverhampton, England

Surface water irrigation of salad crops, defined broadly as those whose aerial parts can be eaten raw, may introduce plant pathogens and may lead to public health problems. Thus enteric disease caused by salmonellae has been reported following the consumption of celery, lettuce and watercress. In the USA the National Technical Advisory Committee proposed an upper faecal coliform limit in water to be used for irrigation of 10 ml^{-1}. Above this limit salmonellae are recoverable from 96·4% of samples (US Department of the Interior Federal Water Pollution Control Administration, 1968). Where water does not meet this standard it has to be treated in some way or not used on a salad crop within four weeks of harvest. It is likely that any EEC Directive on the quality of irrigation water will fall in line with this recommendation.

The high cost of mains water makes the use of surface water increasingly attractive but this must lead inevitably to the risk of plant and/or public health problems. Storage in a reservoir can be used to purify water and the problem becomes one largely of managing water in and water out. In a drought situation the duration of storage may not be sufficient for purification to occur so that some other method is desirable. Ozonization is considered to be too expensive and practical alternatives include chlorination and u.v. radiation. The latter method has several practical advantages over chlorination in that no contact time is needed, corrosion of metal is not a problem, and no chemical taints are likely. Ultraviolet purification of water for public water supplies in rural areas is carried out by several Water Authorities (Jepson, 1973).

The work reported here was carried out to find out if this method could be used to purify river water to an acceptable standard for the irrigation of salad crops, despite known theoretical objections to its use which include the adverse effect of colour, dissolved organic matter, dissolved salts and particulate matter.

Preliminary work, carried out at MAFF Experimental Horticulture Station, Luddington, which compared u.v. radiation with chlorination as a means of treating river water, demonstrated that both treatments were effective in virtually eliminating coliforms. Even when the river was in flood with suspended solids levels as high as 150 mg litre^{-1} and giving the water a cloudy appearance, the percentage "kill" of coliforms by u.v. radiation was of the order of 98% (Adams, 1973).

Resulting from this work a purifier of larger capacity was installed at Luddington in 1975 and used for the treatment of irrigation water in the glasshouse section.

The water was pumped directly to the purifier with no intermediate settlement stage.

In addition to monitoring the purifier a limited number of laboratory observations were made on the effect of u.v. radiation on several bacterial plant pathogens.

Materials and Methods

Ultraviolet purifiers

These were supplied by Pollution Technical Services Ltd, Abingdon, Berkshire (now J. Abay Ltd, Kingston Bagpuize, Abingdon), and were of the low pressure mercury arc lamp type. Model 500SF (maximum capacity 2000 litres hour^{-1}) was used for the initial work at Luddington and the laboratory observations, and model 3000SF (maximum capacity 11 250 litres hour^{-1}) was used for the subsequent work in the glasshouse section at Luddington.

Due to occasional high levels of suspended solids in the river water it was necessary to add two extra pairs of lamps, making eight in all, to model 3000SF in order to maintain the required level of u.v. intensity.

Both purifiers incorporated an electronic "fail-safe" monitor which measured the intensity at 253·7 nm after penetration of the flow medium, and controlled the operation of a solenoid valve which stopped the flow if the intensity fell below the minimum required level.

The bactericidal effectiveness of radiation is given by the survival ratio (% kill) and this ratio is a function of time of exposure and intensity. Ultraviolet intensity is measured in microwatts cm^{-2} and the United States Department of Health requirements for purification of water specifies a minimum dose of 16 000 microwatts seconds cm^{-2} at 253·7 nm u.v. The purifiers used in this work provided a minimum of 30 000 microwatts seconds cm^{-2}.

FIG. 1. The model 500 SF ultraviolet purifier supplied by Pollution Technical Services Ltd and used at Luddington EHS to treat irrigation water, and in the laboratory to assess the effect of u.v. radiation on plant pathogenic bacteria.

Examination of water samples

Water samples were taken at approximately weekly intervals from (1) the River Avon at the point of abstraction, (2) the inlet to the purifier (untreated) and (3) the outlet from the purifier (treated), transported to the laboratory in insulated containers and examined within 6 hours of sampling.

Serial dilutions were prepared in quarter strength Ringer's Solution and examined by Most Probable Number techniques for coliforms, using Minerals Modified Glutamate Medium (Oxoid CM 289) at 37° and Lactose Ricinoleate Broth (Oxoid CM 371) at 44° as a confirmatory test for *Escherichia coli*. The total bacterial count was determined at 22° and 37° using Milk Agar (Oxoid CM 21) and pectate-degrading bacteria were determined by spreading 0·1 ml on the surface of both pectate gel medium (Paton, 1959) and Stewart's Medium (Stewart, 1962).

Laboratory observations

Cultures of plant pathogenic bacteria isolated during routine examination of plant material were used. These were a soft-rotting *Pseudomonas* group IV b (Lelliot *et al.*, 1966), *Pseudomonas marginalis*, *Erwinia carotovora* var. *atroseptica*, *Corynebacterium fasciens*, and a pectate de-grading *Flavobacterium* sp. isolated from cucumber stem. In addition a pectate degrading *Flavobacterium* sp. isolated from the irrigation water was used and a culture of *E. coli* was included because the effect of radiation on this organism is well documented. These observations were made on suspensions of the organisms in clean water so that transmission of radiation was not impaired, with the result that they received in excess of the minimum dose from the equipment.

Results

Water samples from Luddington

The numbers of bacteria in the samples taken directly from the river varied considerably, especially in the summer months when the mud at the bottom of the river was disturbed by the passage of boats close to the abstraction point (Table 1). Pectate-degrading bacteria were isolated from all the samples although not in large numbers.

The amount of contamination was generally not as large in the samples taken at the purifier immediately before treatment compared with the

TABLE 1. Bacteriological analyses of water samples taken directly from the river, and before and after treatment with u.v. radiation

Sample	Colony count ml^{-1}		Most Probable Number 100 ml^{-1}		Pectate degrading bacteria ml^{-1}	
	22°	37°	Coliforms	E. coli	Pectate gel	Stewart's medium
River water						
Min.	5800	840	3500	275	50	10
Max.	184 000	122 000	180 000	180 000	2300	2100
Mean	64 950	24 180	61 710	33 370	950	272
n	17	17	26	26	24	24
Before treatment						
Min.	2970	160	350	0	10	0
Max.	74 000	19 800	160 000	160 000	1900	300
Mean	15 770	3910	23 450	9560	562	40
n	15	15	23	25[a]	19	19
After treatment						
Min.	530	212	0	0	0	0
Max.	50 800	48 000	350	175	2600	200
Mean	13 910	7520	30	17	324	12
n	21	21	27	51[b]	19	19

[a] Two samples examined using 44° incubation only.
[b] 24 samples examined using 44° incubation only.

samples taken from the river, and this would suggest that some settlement had occurred in the pipework between the pump at the river and the purifier, a distance of 400 metres.

Most Probable Numbers of coliforms and *E. coli* were greatly reduced in the water samples taken after treatment. There was little difference in the numbers of pectate-degrading bacteria isolated although they were only found on Stewart's medium in two of the samples.

The percentage "kill" was calculated for pairs of samples taken immediately before and after treatment and was only calculated for pairs of samples where an end point was determined in the Most Probable Number technique. Mean percentage "kill" was 99·08% and 99·55% for coliforms and *E. coli* respectively (23 pairs of samples).

Laboratory observations

The following results were obtained for the percentage "kill" of the test organisms after passage through the u.v. purifier. Two series of observations were carried out for each organism. *Escherichia coli* 100% and 99·99%, *Pseudomonas* group IV b 99·99% and 99·99%, *Pseudomonas marginalis* 99·99% and 99·98%, *E. carotovora* var. *atroseptica* 99·93% and 99·82%, pectolytic *Flavobacterium* sp. from cucumber 99·99 and 99·96%, pectolytic *Flavobacterium* sp. from water 99·99% and 99·98% and for *Corynebacterium fasciens* 99·98% and 99·91%.

Discussion

It is known that *E. coli* has a greater resistance to radiation than other waterborne enteric disease bacteria; therefore it is a suitable test organism for evaluating the effectiveness of u.v. treatment. Examination of the river water samples before and after treatment demonstrated that on average 99·08% of coliforms and 99·55% *E. coli* were "killed" by u.v. radiation. These results were similar to those obtained in the preliminary work at Luddington although the bacteriological quality of the water before treatment was better on that occasion. Thus, in a commercial situation u.v. radiation can be an effective means of treating irrigation water possibly contaminated with enteric disease causing bacteria.

Despite more than 99% of coliforms being "killed" by treatment a large number of bacteria could still be isolated from the water. No attempt was made to identify the surviving organisms but they were possibly spore formers which have a greater resistance to radiation.

With regard to the effectiveness of the system against plant pathogens, numbers of pectate-degrading bacteria were low in the water before treatment and radiation did not reduce their numbers to the same extent as happened with the coliforms.

Identification of all the pectate-degrading bacteria was not attempted although it was noted that the predominant organism recovered on the pectate gel medium before and after treatment was a pectolytic *Flavobacterium* sp. In the laboratory this organism could be effectively "killed" by radiation as were the other plant pathogens. With irrigation water there is always the possibility that suspended matter will protect normally susceptible bacteria to some extent, and this could be the limiting factor in the use of u.v. purification in horticultural and agricultural situations. The incorporation into the equipment of a "fail-safe" device which measures transmission of u.v. radiation will go a long way to overcoming this problem if turbidity in the water is not continuous.

There is a need for further work to be done on the effectiveness of radiation against fungal plant pathogens such as *Pythium* and *Phytophthora*.

References

ADAMS, R. P. (1973). Ultra-violet radiation proves effective means of purifying water in Luddington trials. *The Grower*, May 26, 1212.

JEPSON, J. D. (1973). Disinfection of water supplies by ultra-violet radiation. *Water Treatment and Examination*, **22**, 175–190.

LELLIOT, R. A. *et al.* (1966). A determinative scheme for the fluorescent plant pathogenic pseudomonads. *Journal of Applied Bacteriology*, **29**, 470–489.

PATON, A. M. (1959). An improved method for preparing pectate gels. *Nature, London*, **183**, 1812–1813.

STEWART, D. J. (1962). A selective-diagnostic medium for the isolation of pectinolytic organisms in the enterobacteriaceae. *Nature, London*, **195**, 1023.

US Department of the Interior, Federal Water Pollution Control Administration (1968). *Report of the Committee on Water Quality Criteria.* Cited by GELDREICH E. E. & BORDNER, R. H. (1971) In *Journal of Milk and Food Technology*, **34**, 184–195.

The Bacterial Leaf Nodule Association in *Psychotria*

Lynda M. Fletcher* and Muriel E. Rhodes-Roberts

*Department of Botany and Microbiology, University
College of Wales, Aberystwyth, Wales*

Leaf nodules have been reported to be present in more than 400 species of the two families Myrsinaceae and Rubiaceae. Three genera have received the most attention: *Ardisia* (Myrsinaceae), *Pavetta* and *Psychotria* (Rubiaceae). Symbiotic bacteria are thought to inhabit these leaf nodules, although this has been verified for only a few of these species. The bacterial leaf nodule associations have been discussed by several authors, but the most comprehensive review to date is by Lersten and Horner (1976); this covers all aspects.

The basic problem fundamental to understanding the association, i.e. the isolation and identification of the bacterial endophyte, and its role within the plant, remain unsolved. One of the main reasons for this is the difficulty in obtaining bacteria-free plants to carry out Koch's postulates and thus definitively identify the causative organism(s) and the nature of the association, which is usually described as symbiotic although the detailed relationships are obscure, and non-nodulated species can thrive in the same habitat.

Studies have been carried out at Aberystwyth since 1965 on a plant of *Psychotria mucronata* Hiern. donated by Dr. P. M. Cartwright of the University of Reading. This plant was grown from seed No. C.3004 obtained from Mr. E. E. Kemp, the Curator of the Royal Botanic Garden, Edinburgh, Scotland. Our work has been concentrated on two aspects, namely the isolation and identification of the bacterial endophyte(s), and the production of bacteria-free plants.

The Symbiotic Cycle

The bacterial endophyte is present within the plant throughout all stages of its life cycle, and there is apparently no random infection; the generally accepted cycle is summarized in Fig. 1. Although bacteria are

* Present address: Biology Department, King Alfred's College, Winchester, England.

definitely present between the embryo and endosperm, their exact mode of entry into the seed is not yet known. The only known study of the flowers and seeds in a *Psychotria* species is that of Gordon (1964) on *P. nairobiensis*. He examined serial sections of inflorescences and mature

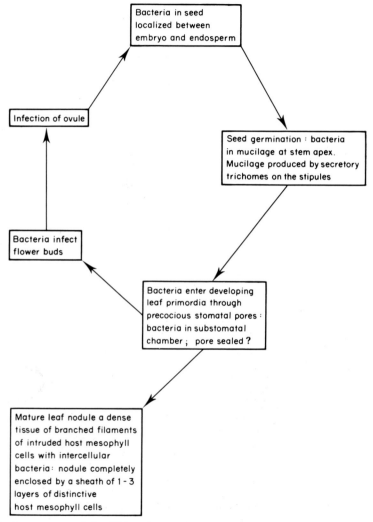

FIG. 1. A summary of the life cycle of the bacterial endophyte in *Psychotria*.

seeds stained with carbol fuchsin, and developing fruits (*ca.* 3 mm diameter) stained with carbol thionin-Orange G. In young closed floral buds all the primordial floral parts were enveloped in a mucilaginous film containing numerous bacteria. Bacteria were also present in the ovarian cavity. In open flowers, remnants of the bacterial film remained only on the surfaces of the sepals, petals and style, and a few bacteria were again observed in the ovarian cavity. Sections of the developing fruits showed that bacteria were present in the immediate vicinity of the developing embryo, whereas a mucilaginous, bacteria-containing layer completely enveloped the embryo in the mature seeds. Gordon did not ascertain from this study the exact mode of entry of the bacteria into the seeds of *P. nairobiensis*, but he suggested that it was probably via the micropyle of the developing ovule, because he found the same type of bacteria concentrated at the site of formation of the micropyle in both the open flower stage, and at the micropylar end of the developing embryo in the seed. We found that seeds of *P. mucronata* germinated readily, but the cotyledons of the seedlings were always unexpectedly non-nodulated, see Fig. 2a. This supports the view that the infection of leaves occurs

FIG. 2. (a) Seedling of *Psychotria mucronata* showing normal nodulated leaves; note absence of nodules on the cotyledons.
(b) *Psychotria nairobiensis*, showing non-nodulated crippled plant, A, and normal plant, B, after 14 months (from Gordon, 1964).

only at the very young leaf primordium stage in the terminal buds; Lersten and Horner (1976) should be consulted for full details of the process of systemic infection of the leaves leading to the development of the more familiar leaf nodule.

Isolation and Identification of the Bacterial Endophyte

At Aberystwyth many attempts have been made, using a wide variety of techniques and media, to isolate bacteria from the leaf nodules of *P. mucronata*. Preliminary findings were reported by Rhodes-Roberts to the Society for Applied Bacteriology in July, 1967 (Belfast meeting), but never published because the 12 *Agrobacterium*-like isolates which were thought to be the most likely symbiont died, and could not be re-isolated from the plants. Since then, about 100 attempts have been made to re-isolate these bacteria, as well as those fully described by Gordon (1964). Batches of *ca*. 100 leaf nodules, and similar areas of non-nodulated leaf tissue as controls, were separately macerated in various diluents using a Gallenkamp glass tissue grinder. The resultant suspensions were used to prepare both pour and spread plates using a wide variety of media, including nutrient agar, glucose nutrient agar, the classic congo red mannitol agar suitable for *Rhizobium*, King's B agar for fluorescent bacteria, and *Psychotria* leaf extract agar. Because it has been claimed that the bacterial endophyte fixes dinitrogen, slight modifications of the "nitrogen-free" *Azotobacter* medium of Brown *et al.* (1962) were included: the modifications consisted of replacing the glucose with sucrose, and/or adding 0·05% Difco yeast extract as a growth factor supplement.

Although it might be expected that leaves or leaf nodule suspensions of *P. mucronata* which had been surface sterilized with 10 volumes of hydrogen peroxide, 0·1% mercuric chloride or 5·0% sodium hypochlorite, might be sterile, it was very surprising that non-sterilized leaf macerates also rarely yielded many micro-organisms; often more than 80·0% of the resultant plates were sterile, and the rest showed an occasional yeast, *Penicillium*, *Cladosporium*, *Bacillus* or yellow *Micrococcus*. Therefore the release of toxic compounds into the macerated leaf suspensions was suspected, although when 12 test strains of various Gram-positive and Gram-negative bacteria were tested, only *Bacillus subtilis* showed any inhibition of growth in the presence of leaf suspensions. Nevertheless, in further experiments, possible protective agents such as starch, serum, sucrose (1–20%), activated charcoal and manganese dioxide, either individually or in combination, were incorporated into both the suspending and plating media. Mere dilution of the concentrated macerates was also investigated. Thus, from such numerous modifications, over 200 isolates of Gram-negative bacteria have been isolated from both leaf nodules and from non-nodulated leaf areas, via pour and spread plates and shake cultures. Further characterization of these bacteria, including tests for nitrogen fixation, are still in progress. So far, the bacteria isolated from leaf nodules and non-nodulated leaf tissue are similar, and include several genera, *Streptomyces, Bacillus, Micrococcus* or *Sarcina*, small Gram-positive rods, *Mycoplana rubra, Flavobacterium, Enterobacter, Erwinia, Klebsiella, Pseudomonas fluorescens, Alcaligenes* and many *Agrobacterium-* or *Rhizobium-* or *Chromobacterium*-like organisms. This wide range of bacteria has been obtained on many occasions. Furthermore, the variety of organisms isolated was very similar on all the agar media used, and the different suspending media did not significantly affect the result obtained (although dilution was important to overcome toxicity). These observations agree with those of Becking (1971) who could not isolate any bacteria from nodulated leaf discs of *P. mucronata* which had been surface sterilized with 75·0% or 96·0% ethanol or 6·0% hydrogen peroxide. Leaf nodules which were not surface sterilized yielded a similar wide range of bacteria as found here. Becking also regarded these as normal epiphytic flora because identical strains were isolated from his other plants with non-nodulated leaves.

When the Aberystwyth plants produced flowers and viable seeds, techniques similar to the above were used to try to isolate the endophyte from the hypocotyls of seedlings grown from surface-sterilized seeds of *P. mucronata*. Again, a wide variety of bacteria has been isolated, both from the hypocotyls derived from surface-sterilized seeds germinated under aseptic conditions, and from unsterilized seed, the hypocotyls of which were surface sterilized prior to maceration. These hypocotyl isolates are currently being characterized in detail for comparison with the nodule and leaf surface isolates.

In our opinion the most careful study of the leaf nodule association was carried out by Gordon (1964). Virtually pure cultures of mucoid bacteria were isolated from suspensions of macerated germinating seeds of *Ardisia crispa* and *P. nairobiensis* on Oxoid nutrient agar. The seeds did not yield absolutely pure cultures, but one type was certainly dominant. From biochemical and physiological tests on purified cultures of these two isolates (one from each host), they were identified as the same type. Gram-negative bacteria morphologically similar to these isolates were seen in the living plants and seeds of *A. crispa* and *P. nairobiensis* by microscopic examination of variously stained sections. Furthermore, Gordon (1964) located the same bacterium *in situ* in these two species by means of a labelled fluorescent antiserum which was prepared against the bacterial isolate obtained from the *P. nairobiensis* seedling. This anti-serum has also been shown to react with the bacteria in various tissues of other leaf-nodulated species of *Pavetta* (*Pavetta grandiflora*) and *Psychotria* (*Psychotria emetica*) as reported by Bettelheim *et al.* (1968). The antiserum showed no reaction with the tissues of *Ardisia elliptica*, a non-nodulated species.

Gordon (1964) tentatively identified this bacterium as a species of *Rhizobium*, but when this work was extended by Bettelheim *et al.* (1968) the name *Chromobacterium lividum* was thought to be more correct. However, in 1967 at Belfast, Rhodes-Roberts expressed the opinion that the true leaf nodule endophyte more closely resembled an agrobacterium (based upon the properties of the leaf nodule isolates which subsequently died and could not be re-isolated). At Aberystwyth many *Agrobacterium*-like (or indeed *Rhizobium*-like) organisms have been isolated from both the leaf nodules and the hypocotyls of seedlings, together with the epiphytes already listed.

Many different bacteria have been claimed by different workers to be the endophyte. Most of the candidates have also been isolated here from *P. mucronata*, but the exact identity of the causative agent still remains uncertain because of the difficulty in obtaining bacteria-free plants for experimental inoculation. An excellent review of the confused nomenclature relevant to the identity of the various leaf nodule bacteria described in the literature is given by Horner and Lersten (1972).

Production of Bacteria-free Plants

The spontaneous production of non-nodulated dwarf plants, thought to be bacteria-free, from plants which normally show leaf nodules, was described by Miehe (1919), Humm (1944) and Becking (1971). Such dwarf plants were often both stunted and deformed, and thus came to be known as "cripples". Later it was shown that cripples could be produced experimentally by heat treating seeds such that the bacterial symbiont was killed, without impairing germination. From several studies on a number of different leaf-nodulated plant species, different time-temperature combinations have been reported to yield bacteria-free plants: 50° for 25 min (von Faber, 1912), 40° for 48 h (Miehe, 1919), 50° for 10 min and 52° for 7 min (de Jongh, 1938). Only two workers have attempted this on seed of *Psychotria* spp. Becking (1971) reported good results using the methodology of Miehe (1919). However, using *P. nairobiensis*, Gordon (1964) concluded that 52° for 10 min was the most effective heat treatment; the resultant cripple plants of *P. nairobiensis* (see Fig. 2b) showed abnormalities very similar to those described for *A. crispa* (Miehe, 1919; de Jongh, 1938). The heat treatment seemed not to affect seed germination, and initially there were no morphological differences between the control and treated seedlings. However, after four months, plants from heat-treated seeds had short stems (*ca.* 2 cm), an average of three small, thin, twisted pale yellow leaves and a swollen terminal bud. Control plants averaged 6 cm height and six leaves. The terminal bud of the cripples was subsequently replaced by several smaller buds which developed into irregular protuberances. After one year, when these plants averaged 8 cm height, no further stem growth occurred. Gordon's crippled plants died after 2–3 years. At Aberystwyth a few crippled plants of *P. mucronata* have been produced by this method (3 out of 36 heat-treated seeds produced cripples), and we confirmed that heat-treatment (52° 10 min^{-1}) did not affect the rate of germination; indeed, in one experiment the heat-treated seeds germinated faster than the untreated seed.

Gordon (1964) noticed that his pathetic cripple plants were not always nodule free, and in stained sections of such nodules on the crippled leaves of *P. nairobiensis* he found bacteria. Moreover, he extended the observations of Miehe (1919) that non-nodulated cripple plants frequently reverted spontaneously to normal growth; in one experiment, 11 out of 19 plants from heated (52° 10 min^{-1}) seeds were cripples at four months, but after nine months only four were still dwarfed. This emphasizes the need for adequate controls and considerable patience when interpreting experiments involving inoculations of crippled plants to elucidate the causative nodulating organism(s); it possibly explains the apparently successful *Klebsiella rubiacearum* inoculation experiments of Centifanto and Silver (1964).

The effect of heat treatment on the seed itself is not known and so other methods for obtaining bacteria-free plants have been investigated. The first attempt to obtain such plants by means of tissue culture was described by von Faber (1912). His attempts were unsuccessful and the technique received no further attention until LaMotte and Lersten (1972) reported the production of *P. punctata* Vatke callus tissue bearing abundant roots, see Fig. 3a. The medium which supported stem callus tissue growth at the fastest rate, and also induced good root formation, was adopted as their "stock callus medium". Details of this medium, and the later modification of it used by Edwards (1974), together with the methods used to sterilize the plant tissue inoculum, are given in the Appendix. LaMotte and Lersten used young stem internodes for the initiation of callus tissue because the bacterial symbiont is generally assumed to be confined to leaf buds, leaf nodules and seeds. Neither workers reported on the methods used for checking the sterility of the

FIG. 3 (a) *Psychotria punctata* callus tissue grown in the dark in 125 ml flasks. (1) Callus tissue from young stem internodes after 7 weeks on the stock callus medium. Note numerous erect to obliquely orientated roots; right arrow shows root grown into agar, left arrows indicate roots which ceased growth at the agar surface. (2) Internode explant after 4–5 weeks on Linsmaier and Skoog (1965) medium, with callus at ends and flank. (3) On left, tobacco callus without roots; on right *Psychotria* callus with roots, after 12 weeks on the stock callus medium (from LaMotte and Lersten, 1972).

8 cm

(b) *Psychotria mucronata* callus tissue grown in the dark on 50 ml of the basal medium of Edwards (1974) plus 0·5 mg litre⁻¹ kinetin and 5 mg litre⁻¹ indole-3-acetic acid in a 100 ml flask, from a surface-sterilized stem explant inoculated 19.7.76; photographed 6.10.76. Note 2 small roots.

resultant callus tissue. It is not sufficient to rely on the appearance of visible bacterial growth on the callus agar because it has a pH value of 5·2; dormant bacteria may well be present. The sterility of the *P. mucronata* callus tissue produced in this laboratory, see Fig. 3b, was checked by macerating samples of it in sterile nutrient broth, and then streaking the suspensions on a wide variety of media suitable for the growth of a wide range of plant-associated bacteria. Only three out of seven separate callus tissues obtained from different stem explants were found to be completely sterile. Furthermore, in the light of Hayward's timely review (1974) on latent bacteria in plant tissues, our fairly extensive tests were still inadequate to conclude that the remaining three callus tissue cultures were bacteria free. Careful and continuous monitoring of tissue cultures is thus essential.

To induce shoot formation, and finally obtain bacteria-free plants is proving to be much more difficult. However, the results of Edwards (1974) experiments (now published by Edwards and LaMotte, 1976) were most encouraging, as is shown in Fig. 4. He cultured explanted terminal buds of *P. punctata* on the basal medium (see Appendix) plus the plant growth factor from maize, zeatin—6-(4-hydroxy-3-methyl but-2-enyl) amino purine—(now a commercially available cytokinin) in concentrations ranging from 10^{-7} to 10^{-4} M. These were kept under three different environmental conditions; a greenhouse, a laboratory cabinet illuminated by continuous incandescent light, and a similar dark cabinet in the same room. The cabinet temperature was $24 \pm 1°$. Only those cultures maintained in a greenhouse during June and July formed buds on the callus proliferating from the bases of the excised terminal buds, and only when supplied with 10^{-4} to 10^{-5} M zeatin (see Fig. 4). When this experiment was repeated in the greenhouse in September of the same year, very little callus and no buds were formed. The summer temperatures had been significantly higher, up to $45°$ on clear days. Further experiments were thus performed in controlled environment chambers, with 8- and 16-h lengths of daylight, and a temperature of $27 \pm 1°$ in the dark period and $32 \pm 1°$ in the light (19 375–20 451 lux) period. Shoots with nodulated leaves grew directly from the terminal buds to an equal extent in both photoperiods. Callus tissue was produced from the base of the explants, but this (with one exception) did not initiate any buds and subsequent shoots such as had occurred in the greenhouse in summer. More callus grew in the 8-h than in the 16-h light period routine. In the absence of zeatin, the terminal buds produced only small shoots representing only the expansion of the terminal buds, and little or no basal callus tissue.

FIG. 4. *Psychotria punctata* explants. (1) Surface-sterilized terminal buds cultured for 4 weeks in the greenhouse on slightly modified stock callus medium of LaMotte and Lersten (1972), with 4 concentrations of zeatin, during June–July 1973. Left to right, 10^{-7}, 10^{-6}, 10^{-5} and 10^{-4} M zeatin. (2) Buds (arrowed) on callus originating at base of excised sterilized terminal bud of *Psychotria* after 4 weeks on basal stock callus medium plus 10^{-4} M zeatin (June–July, 1973). (3) Bud (arrowed) from culture grown as in (2) except that the medium contained 10^{-5} M zeatin. (4) Shoots (arrowed) arising directly from sterilized terminal buds of *Psychotria* after 10 weeks on basal stock callus medium plus 10^{-4} M zeatin in 16-h daylight in a controlled environment chamber. (5) Same as (4); arrows indicate leaf nodules. (6) Terminal buds after 10 weeks in culture on stock callus basal medium without auxin or cytokinin. Buds (sterilized) had been cultured in 16-h daylight in a controlled environment chamber. (7) Showing the effects of gentamicin on surface-sterilized terminal buds cultured for 10 weeks on basal medium plus 10^{-4} M zeatin in a controlled environment chamber. Left to right: 10, 50, 100 and 200 mg litre^{-1} gentamicin. Note that the left flask has a shoot with nodules (from Edwards, 1974).

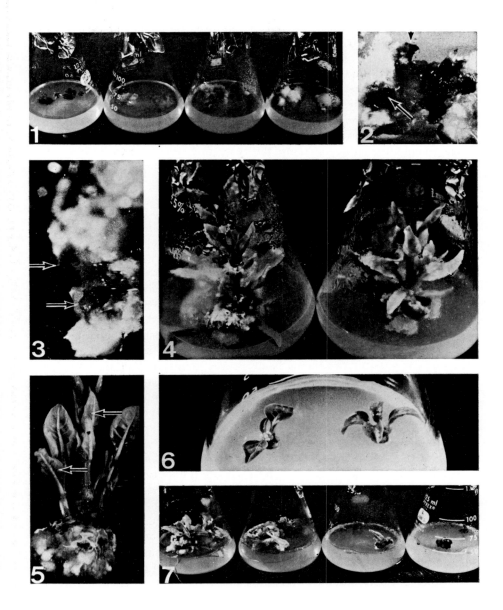

In the above experiments the bacteria in the terminal bud explants had obviously not been killed by the ethanol and sodium hypochlorite sterilization techniques employed. Therefore gentamicin at concentrations from 50 to 200 mg litre^{-1} was added to the callus medium containing 10^{-4} M zeatin: Edwards found that shoot development was then completely inhibited (see Fig. 4). The lowest antibiotic concentration tested (10 mg litre^{-1}) permitted shoot development but it did not eliminate the bacteria; these shoots were clearly nodulated (Fig. 4). Edwards (1974) concluded that callus tissue of *P. punctata* required an exceptionally high concentration of exogenous cytokinin (zeatin), plus a midsummer greenhouse light and temperature regime, for buds to be initiated from callus derived from terminal buds. Whether a high temperature, a high light intensity, a long photoperiod or some critical combination of all these factors, is essential, is discussed by Edwards and LaMotte (1976). Successful tissue culture from woody plants such as *Psychotria* has rarely been reported: useful reviews relevant to tissue culture of herbaceous plants are those of Murashige (1974), Street (1973) and Yeoman (1973).

A greenhouse observation by Becking (1971) is pertinent to the nodulation phenomenon. He noted that a plant of *P. mucronata* which had been cut down to near soil level produced three new shoots; the leaves on two of these were nodulated, but those of the third were nodule free. Despite this, the non-nodulated shoot was of almost normal size and appearance, and not dramatically crippled. This suggested another method for possibly producing bacteria-free plants, and so in December 1975, 30 of our normal nodulated plants of *P. mucronata* were cut back close to the soil level. The new shoots which were initiated were sometimes normal (with nodulated leaves), sometimes abnormal (usually with extremely small nodules) or a mixture of both types on the same plant; the three types are illustrated in Fig. 5. On plants with both types of shoot, the abnormal shoots usually were more stunted than the normal ones, see Fig. 5b, and the apical meristem was often distorted and frequently died, see Fig. 6c, and the leaves near to the apex were also especially crinkled or distorted, as in Fig. 5c and Fig. 6c. The leaves of typical normal and abnormal plants are shown in Fig. 6a, b. On the abnormal shoots the leaves were markedly darker green and glossier, as is evident in Fig. 5b, and altogether showed very similar characteristics to the nodule-free plants obtained by Becking (1971), who called such plants "cripples". These are, however, very different from the crippled plants of *P. nairobiensis*, Fig. 2b, derived from heat-treated seeds by Gordon (1964). The dark green leaves of Becking-type cripples were often normal in size and shape, Fig. 6b, but on careful examination very small nodules, only just visible to the naked eye, were usually noticed on abnormal leaves after *ca.* 6 months in the greenhouse. Therefore, in the same way that Gordon's cripples had to be observed closely, and for at least 6 months, to determine whether they were nodulated or not, equal care and patience is necessary in any attempt to obtain bacteria-free shoots by hard pruning.

Nature of the Association

The bacterial leaf nodule-plant association is almost always referred to as a symbiosis, although a definition of the relationship remains hypothetical. There are two main theories postulating the nature of the symbiosis, either that the bacterial endophyte is capable of fixing dinitrogen, or that it produces one or more plant growth-regulating substances: possibly both functions are involved. These viewpoints are fully discussed by Fletcher (1976) and Lersten and Horner (1976). The nitrogen-fixing theory stems from the positive results obtained by von Faber (1912, 1914) and the obvious analogies with the exhaustively studied leguminous root nodule system. There are many controversial reports of both positive and negative results of tests for nitrogen fixation using both old (Kjeldahl) and new (acetylene reduction) test methods, and either pure cultures of bacteria isolated from nodules or seedlings, nodulated leaves or whole plants. Greenhouse experiments involving nitrogen balance sheets to show a net uptake of nitrogen, especially for plants growing in nitrogen-deficient soils, have also been undertaken by several workers from von Faber (1912, 1914) to Becking (1971), but the conclusions are often equivocal. To these we can add our quota: we have certainly confirmed that both the *Ardisia crispa* and *P. nairobiensis* isolates of Gordon (1964), and the *Klebsiella rubiacearum* of Silver *et al.* (1963) *usually* showed reduction of acetylene to ethylene in this laboratory. We have experimented with many different growth conditions (age, medium and temperature) for the test cultures, and several different gas mixtures (of argon, oxygen, carbon dioxide and acetylene) in the acetylene reduction test, to try to elucidate the puzzling causes of variable results in replicated cultures and in the controls. On one occasion five out of the six "sterile blanks" contained abundant ethylene. We have been bedevilled with systems producing ethylene endogenously in the absence of any added acetylene, by ethylene production from the polythene tubing of the gassing apparatus when it was kept in a chamber containing u.v. light, and by an ubiquitous *Bacillus* sp. (detected in the "sterile" controls), which seemed to emanate from the cylinder of acetylene. Thus the sporadic occurrences of acetylene reduction by the

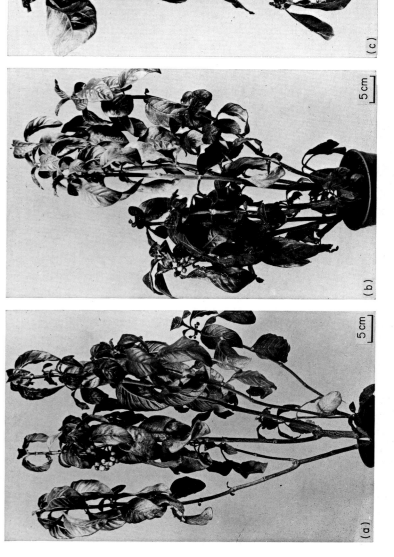

Fig. 5. *Psychotria mucronata* plants photographed October 1976 from plants which had been cut back down to near soil level in December 1975 and grown in our heated (25°) greenhouse in John Innes compost No. 2 with an 18 : 6 light : dark cycle maintained by 700 W and 400 W Hg vapour lamps. (a) Plant with all shoots normal and nodulated; note fruits. (b) Plant with both normal nodulated, and abnormally nodulated shoots. Very small nodules were usually seen. Note darker colour of abnormal shoots, which also produced flowers; note the fruits on the abnormal branches. (c) Plant with all shoots abnormal; leaf nodules absent or very small. Many leaves markedly crinkled or distorted, but plants flowered and fruited (berry evident on lower right branch).

Fig. 6. Enlargements from plants of *Psychotria mucronata* described in Fig. 5. to show (a) the leaf of a normal shoot with conspicuous nodules, (b) a leaf from an abnormal shoot with no readily-visible nodules and (c) a deformed shoot apex on an abnormal branch bearing leaves which were often distorted; note the normal-looking fruit (left centre).

above cultures and our own seedling hypocotyl and leaf nodule isolates are still being investigated. We have over 200 isolates which have survived subculture on nitrogen-free media for periods up to 10 years; their growth is often rapid and abundant and if this reflects mere scavenging of traces of combined nitrogen compounds, it is an extremely efficient survival process.

It is now increasingly appreciated that the beneficial effects of many classic nitrogen-fixing bacteria such as *Azotobacter* may in fact reside more in their ability to synthesize and excrete factors markedly stimulatory to plant growth, than in their nitrogen-fixing capacity, e.g. as shown by Barea and Brown (1974) for *Azotobacter paspali*. That this might also apply to the nodule endophyte was appreciated by De Jongh (1938), who tried to reverse the crippled growth of stunted *Ardisia crispa* plants by treating them with β-indolyl-acetic acid. This was not effective. Silver *et al.* (1963) similarly applied gibberellins externally to crippled plants of *P. punctata* and obtained a slight enhancement of growth compared with control plants. Becking (1971), more comprehensively investigated the effects of solutions of four plant growth substances, indole-3-acetic acid, gibberellic acid, kinetin (a cytokinin) and benzyladenine, at various concentrations, on crippled plants of *P. mucronata*. Only gibberellic acid at 1.0 mg ml^{-1} increased the growth of these stunted plants, by 10–15 cm in 1·5 months compared with untreated plants.

Becking also noted that chlorophyll was degraded less rapidly round the nodules of senescing leaves of *P. mucronata*, and he reasoned that this might be due to the well-known "chlorophyll retention effect" of cytokinin. He demonstrated the accumulation of cytokinin in leaf nodules by placing leaf nodule and leaf matrix discs on excised oat leaf blades; delayed chlorophyll breakdown was strikingly demonstrable in the oat leaves only in the presence of nodules. Furthermore, Becking (1971) demonstrated "cytokinin-induced directed transport" of ^{14}C-labelled α-amino isobutyric acid from the point of its application at the tips of the leaves; the macro-autoradiographs showed the accumulation of the labelled compound in the leaf nodules. More recently, Edwards and LaMotte (1975) confirmed analytically that nodulated portions of *P. punctata* leaves contained from 100 to 2000 × more cytokinin (using zeatin as a standard) than non-nodulated portions of the leaves.

The production of cytokinin(s) by pure cultures of Gordon's *Chromobacterium lividum* NCTC 10591, and the *Bacterium foliicola*-like organism of Miehe (1919) isolated from germinated seeds of *Ardisia crispa* by Rodrigues Pereira *et al.* (1972), was convincingly shown by the latter using soy bean callus and radish cotyledon bioassay methods. This, together with Becking's demonstration of cytokinin production *in situ* in *Psycho-*

tria leaf nodules, and the fact that the *P. punctata* callus tissues of Edwards (1974) required exceptionally high levels of exogenous cytokinins to induce shoots, all support the speculations that the endophyte may produce stimulatory or essential cytokinin(s) in the leaf nodules.

Our own limited observations confirm that the association between the bacterial endophyte and the host plant ranges from apparently obligate (as judged by the extreme bacteria-free cripples of Gordon, which however frequently reverted spontaneously to normal nodulated plants), to a non-essential association; this was demonstrated by the induction of shoots of almost normal appearance, except for the absence of conspicuous nodules, by the hard pruning procedure of Becking. Nonnodulated leaves on separate branches of trees of nodulated species have also often been noticed in the field or forest, but in such situations the absence of bacteria in the tissues has not been proven. Alternatively, bacterial products from the neighbouring branches bearing nodulated leaves may have been translocated to the apparently bacteria-free shoots. Nevertheless, one must remember that many non-nodulated species can flourish in the same habitat. Whether, for a given host, the bacterial association is indeed a facultative or obligate symbiosis is still debatable and biologically intriguing.

We believe that the most probable causative organism is Gordon's (1964) *Chromobacterium lividum*, which, according to Rodrigues Pereira *et al.* completely matches Miehe's (1919) *Bacterium foliicola.* An extension of the careful cytological studies of Gordon (1964) using specific fluorescent antisera would probably be highly rewarding in the search for definite answers to some of the many outstanding questions, not least of which is the inability to isolate the endophyte directly from the nodules. We believe that we achieved this once, on 6 June, 1966, but the *Agrobacterium*-like cultures died during the upheaval of a move to a new building. *Mycoplasma* spp. in plant tissues became known at about that time, and so since 1967 we have attempted re-isolations from nodules using sucrose-augmented suspending fluids and media, on the grounds that the nodule organism was perhaps in an L-phase or mycoplasma form. The media now used for the successful culture of plant mycoplasmas, e.g. *Spiroplasma citri*, are obvious candidates for further investigations.

Acknowledgements

We wish to express our sincere appreciation to Dr. J. F. Gordon and the University of London for permission to reproduce Fig. LXVIII of his thesis as our Fig. 2b: also to Drs. C. E. LaMotte, N. R. Lersten, H. T.

Horner Jr and W. J. Edwards of the Department of Botany and Plant Pathology, Iowa State University, Ames, Iowa, USA for their gifts of photographs for Figs 3a and 4. The permission of the *American Journal of Botany* and the publishers of the *Proceedings of the Iowa Academy of Science* is also acknowledged for Figs 3a and 4 respectively. We are further indebted to the following members of our department: to Mr. D. Parker who has maintained all our greenhouse plants, and to Mrs. G. Hall for technical assistance in the bacteriological studies. Mr. D. Chamberlain provided all the photographs, and Miss H. Bigwood all the art work, both for this paper and for the more extensive original demonstration at the meeting in October 1976.

Appendix

Stock callus medium

The stock callus medium of LaMotte and Lersten (1972) is a modification of the Linsmaier and Skoog (1965) medium. ANALAR reagents are used where available, and glass distilled water is used throughout. The major and minor elements may be made up as separate, concentrated, stock solutions (see 1, 2 and 3 below); they do not have to be autoclaved separately, but should be stored in the cold room (not more than one month). The final compostion of the medium is as shown below.

1.	Potassium nitrate (KNO_3)	1400 mg
	calcium chloride ($CaCl_2 . 2H_2O$)	440 mg
	magnesium sulphate ($MgSO_4 . 7H_2O$)	370 mg
	dipotassium hydrogen phosphate (K_2HPO_4)	425 mg
	sodium ethylenediamine tetra-acetate (Na_2EDTA)	37·3 mg
	ferrous sulphate ($FeSO_4 . 7H_2$)	27·8 mg
2.	Boric acid (H_3BO_3)	6·2 mg
	manganous sulphate ($MnSO_4 . 4H_2O$)	22·3 mg
	zinc sulphate ($ZnSO_4 . 4H_2O$)	8·6 mg
	potassium iodide (KI)	0·83 mg
	sodium molybdenate ($Na_2MoO_4 . 2H_2O$)	0·25 mg
	copper sulphate ($CuSO_4 . 5H_2O$)	0·025 mg
	cobalt chloride ($CoCl_2 . 6H_2O$)	0·025 mg
3.	Thiamine hydrochloride	0·4 mg
	myo-inositol	100 mg
	lactalbumin hydrolysate (Edamin Type S, Sheffield Chemical Co.)	1320 mg
	kinetin	0·5 mg
	3-indole acetic acid	5·0 mg
	Sucrose	30 g
	agar (Oxoid Purified L28 used here)	10 g
	glass distilled water	1·0 litre.

The pH is adjusted to 5·6 with 1 N NaOH; distributed in 50 ml volumes in Erlenmeyer flasks and autoclaved for 20 min at 121°. The final pH is 5·2

Edward's (*1974*) basal medium

This is identical to the stock callus medium of LaMotte and Lersten (1972) except that the dipotassium hydrogen phosphate (K_2HPO_4) is replaced by potassium dihydrogen phosphate (KH_2PO_4) and the 3-indole acetic acid and kinetin are deleted.

Experimental procedures to induce callus tissues and bud formation
Edwards (1974) excised main and branch shoots of *Psychotria punctata* Vatke (= *P. bacteriophila* Val.) grown in the greenhouse. They were washed with 95 % (v/v) ethanol and immersed in half-strength commercial bleach (Miracle Bleach 5·25 % w/v sodium hypochlorite) for 10 min. After several rinses in sterile water, terminal buds were aseptically removed. Three buds each *ca.* 3 mm × 3 mm and bearing 4–6 pairs of leaf primordia were placed on 50 ml volumes of Edward's (1974) basal medium.

References

BAREA, J. M. & BROWN, M. E. (1974). Effects on plant growth produced by *Azotobacter paspali* related to synthesis of plant growth regulating substances. *Journal of Applied Bacteriology*, 37, 583–593.

BECKING, J. H. (1971). The physiological significance of the leaf nodules of *Psychotria*. *Plant and Soil, Special Volume*, 1971, 361–374.

BETTELHEIM, K. A., GORDON, J. F. & TAYLOR, J. (1968). The detection of a strain of *Chromobacterium lividum* in the tissues of certain leaf-nodulated plants by the immunofluorescence technique. *Journal of General Microbiology*, 54, 177–184.

BROWN, M. E., BURLINGHAM, S. K. & JACKSON, R. M. (1962). Studies on *Azotobacter* species in soil. I. Comparison of media and techniques for counting *Azotobacter* in soil. *Plant and Soil*, 17, 309–319.

CENTIFANTO, T. M. & SILVER, W. S. (1964). Leaf nodule symbiosis. I. Endophyte of *Psychotria bacteriophila*. *Journal of Bacteriology*, 88, 776–781.

DE JONGH, Ph. (1938). On the symbiosis of *Ardisia crispa* (Thunb.) A.DC. *Verhandelingen de Koninklijke Nederlandsche Akademie van Wetenschappen Afdeling Natuurkunde* Sect. II, 37, 1–74.

EDWARDS, W. J. (1974). Chemical and physical factors controlling bud formation in *Psychotria punctata*; evidence for an involvement of cytokinins in its leaf nodule symbiosis. M.Sc. thesis, Iowa State University.

EDWARDS, W. J. & LAMOTTE, C. E. (1975). Evidence for cytokinin in bacterial leaf nodules of *Psychotria punctata* (Rubiaceae). *Plant Physiology*, 56, 425–428.

EDWARDS, W. J. & LAMOTTE, C. E. (1976). Bud formation and shoot development *in vitro*: observations on stem and bud explants of *Psychotria punctata* (Rubiaceae). *Proceedings of the Iowa Academy of Science*, 83, 130–132.

FLETCHER, L. M. (1976). Bacterial symbioses in the leaf nodules of Myrsinaceae and Rubiaceae. In *Microbiology of aerial plant surfaces* (Dickinson, C. H. & Preece, T. F., eds). London and New York, Academic Press, pp. 465–485.

GORDON, J. F. (1964). The nature and distribution within the plant of the bacteria associated with certain leaf-nodulated species of the families Myrsinaceae and Rubiaceae. Ph.D. thesis, University of London.

HAYWARD, A. C. (1974). Latent infections by bacteria. *Annual Review of Phytopathology*, 12, 87–97.

HORNER, H. T. Jr & LERSTEN, N. R. (1972). Nomenclature of bacteria in leaf nodules of the families Myrsinaceae and Rubiaceae. *International Journal of Systematic Bacteriology*, 22, 117–122.

HUMM, H. J. (1944). Bacterial leaf nodules. *Journal of the New York Botanical Gardens*, 45, 193–199.

LaMOTTE, C. E. & LERSTEN, N. R. (1972). Attempts to obtain bacteria-free plants of *Psychotria punctata* (Rubiaceae): growth and root formation in callus cultures. *American Journal of Botany*, 59, 89–96.

LERSTEN, N. R. & HORNER, H. T. Jr (1976). Bacterial leaf nodule symbiosis in angiosperms with emphasis on Rubiaceae and Myrsinaceae. *The Botanical Review*, 42, 145–214.

LINSMAIER, E. M. & SKOOG, F. (1965). Organic growth factor requirements of tobacco tissue cultures. *Physiologia Plantarum*, 18, 386–402.

MIEHE, H. (1919). Weitere Untersuchungen über die Bakteriensymbiose bei *Ardisia crispa* II. Die Pflanze ohne Bakterien. *Jahrbuch für Wissenschaftliche Botanik*, 58, 29–65.

MURASHIGE, T. (1974). Plant propagation through tissue cultures. *Annual Review of Plant Physiology*, 25, 135–166.

RODRIGUES PEREIRA, A. S., HOUWEN, P. J. W., DEURENBERG-VOS, H. W. J. & DEY, E. B. F. (1972). Cytokinins and the bacterial symbiosis of *Ardisia* species. *Zeitschrift für Pflanzenphysiologie*, 68, 170–177.

SILVER, W. S., CENTIFANTO, M. & NICHOLAS, D. J. D. (1963). Nitrogen fixation by the leaf-nodule endophyte (*Klebsiella* sp.) of *Psychotria bacteriophila* (Rubiaceae). *Nature, London*, 199, 396–397.

STREET, H. E. (1973). Laboratory organization. In *Plant tissue and cell culture*. (Street, H. E., ed.). Oxford: Blackwell Scientific Publications, pp. 11–30.

VON FABER, F. C. (1912). Das erbliche Zusammenleben von Bakterien und tropischen Pflanzen. *Jahrbuch für Wissenschaftliche Botanik*, 51, 285–375.

VON FABER, F. C. (1914). Die Bakteriensymbiose der Rubiaceen. *Jahrbuch für Wissenschaftliche Botanik*, 54, 243–264.

YEOMAN, M. M. (1973). Tissue (callus) culture-techniques. In *Plant tissue and cell culture* (Street, H. E., ed.). Oxford: Blackwell Scientific Publications, pp. 31–59.

Subject Index